URBAN AGRICULTURE IN ZIMBABWE

Urban Agriculture in Zimbabwe

Implications for urban management and poverty

BEACON MBIBA

Avebury

Aldershot • Brookfield USA • Hong Kong • Singapore • Sydney

Published by
Avebury
Ashgate Publishing Limited
Gower House
Croft Road
Aldershot
Hants GU11 3HR
England

Ashgate Publishing Company
Old Post Road
Brookfield
Vermont 05036
USA

A catalogue record for this book is available from the British Library

ISBN 1 85628 857 9

Library of Congress Catalog Card Number: 95-79656

Typeset by
Chiedza Venekai Mauchaza
P.O. Box MP 203
Mount Pleasant
Harare, Zimbabwe

Printed in Great Britain by Ipswich Book Co. Ltd., Ipswich, Suffolk.

Contents

S
473
.Z55
m39
1995

v

List of Figures

List of Maps

List of Plates

List of Tables

About the Author

Beacon Mbiba is a lecturer at the Department of Rural and Urban Planning, University of Zimbabwe, Co-ordinator of the Urban Agriculture Research Project and member on the RUPSEA Network Secretariat (Association of Rural and Urban Planners in Southern and Eastern Africa). A former civil servant in the Ministry of Local Government for Rural and Urban Development, Harare, his research interests include urban environment and management, urban poverty and geographic information systems for urban management. He studied in Zimbabwe and The Netherlands and has travelled extensively in the SADC region.

Dedication

To my mother, Sosana and my late grandmother Firamwi who tilled the soil and brew *mhanga* to raise cash for my travel to boarding school. To my late uncle Stephen who taught me the value of discipline. And to all my brothers and sisters and our father who worked the cotton fields under the scorching Mwenezi sun.

Acknowledgements

To talk of urban agriculture could be a reversal of development expectations. As Mbeki puts it, ". . . Africa's problem . . . is that people have low expectations. They are willing to accept low standards, live off subsistence agriculture, wear the same set of clothes for weeks on end and walk instead of riding a bicycle or motorbike. We should encourage expectations . . . *We accept spent, corrupt and inferior leadership, take up cheap foreign ideas and so called expatriate expertise* . . . "[1] Or may be in Zimbabwe we expect too much in our cities beyond our resources.

There is no doubt that urban agriculture, especially cultivation of staple foods, is of value to urban households. But how much should we expect from this activity in terms of long term development? The ideas encouraging incorporation of urban agriculture in sustainable city development in Africa are largely driven by foreign protagonists. Do these ideas conform to our expectations of what the city should be? How much do we know of the content and process of urban agriculture and how does it relate to other processes in the city? How does it impact on urban economies, food availability, the environment, infrastructure provision and city politics? Urban agriculture is a prevalent activity on which divergent views exist. Can we establish a common position as to the value of this activity? Too many questions for a single book like this to answer.

This book is a product of a minimalist agenda. Initially I set out to understand the basics of the phenomenon of urban agriculture in Zimbabwe. It has been a pleasant surprise to find that the topic is more diverse than most people reckon. More surprising was to see that output from my efforts found a ready audience both locally and internationally and that soon, some of it will be a basis for practical urban agriculture projects in the country. The book is just a beginning - more is still to be done before urban agriculture's contribution to sustainable city development is maximised. As development policy shifts from the rural to an urban bias in the late 1990s, urban agriculture will receive greater recognition than in the past.

I had few companions during the early stages of my work as most professionals were still very sceptical about urban agriculture. Professor Kadmiel Wekwete, Andrew Mlalazi and Dr Bert Helmsing were in this group. Convincing them of urban agriculture as a relevant research and policy topic became an objective as I trudged along. I am very grateful for their critical questions many of which are still to be answered and am happy that they now view urban agriculture in a more positive way. Many other people and institutions assisted me in a variety of ways and I thank them all.

My colleagues in the Department of Rural and Urban Planning, University of Zimbabwe provided research facilities, office space and a pleasant working environment, colleagues at the Institute of Social Studies (The Hague), those in the RUPSEA Network, the GRUPHEL Network as well as those in the Department of Town and Country Planning, University of Sheffield gave support all the way. Many of my students assisted on field work exercises, I thank them too. The Harare City Council, Chitungwiza Town Council, Sheffield City Council and The Herald (Harare) deserve a special thank you for making their files, materials and staff available to facilitate my ongoing research.

My wife Tendai and our children Tonderai and Makomborero gave a lot of support over the years, many thanks.

Nodumo Tshuma of the UZ Medical School and Andrew Banda of the Geography Department assisted with the photographic work while Mrs Julia White and Samuel Matsangaize did the editing and Chiedza Mauchaza did the typesetting. Their contributions will always be remembered. Some chapters of the book are upgraded versions of journal and conference papers. All persons and institutions which provided these avenues for dissemination of my output are sincerely thanked.

I hope this book will make its small contribution to this very important feature of our urban areas.

Notes

1   Moeletsi Mbeki, page 13, Development and Democracy; Africa and Asia; Issues for South Africa, December 1994 (with emphasis by the author)

Abbreviations

%	percent
ANOVA	Analysis of Variance
C.S.O.	Central Statistical Office, Zimbabwe
D.W.F.	Dry Weather Flow
DCIA	Departmental Committee of Inquiry Into Allotments, Her Majesty's Stationary Office, (1969), UK
DHCS	Department of Housing and Community Services
Dr	Doctor
ENDA	Environment, Development Activities
ESAP	Economic Structural Adjustment Programme
GMB	Grain Marketing Board
GRUPHEL	Gender Research, Urbanisation, Planning, Housing and Everyday Life
gvt. or Gvt.	Government
H/Q	Headquarters
IDRC	International Development Research Centre, Canada
ILO	International Labour Organisation
kg	kilogram
M.A.S.	Modified Activated Sludge
MLAWD	Ministry of Lands, Agriculture and Water Development
MPSLSW	Ministry of Public Service, Labour and Social Welfare
MSU	Municipal Security Unit
NGOs	Non-Governmental Organisation(s)
No.	number
NRB	Natural Resources Board
pp	page
RUP	Department of Rural and Urban Planning, University of Zimbabwe

RUPSEA	Association of Rural and Urban Planners in Southern and Eastern Africa
SDA	Social Dimensions of Adjustment
SDF	Social Dimensions Fund
UK	United Kingdom
UNDP	United Nations Development Programme
UNICEF	United Nations Children's Fund
US$	United States dollar
USAID	United States Agency for International Development
UZ	University of Zimbabwe
WHO	World Health Organisation
Z$	Zimbabwe dollar
ZANU (PF)	Zimbabwe African National Union (Patriotic Front)
ZESA	Zimbabwe Electricity Supply Authority
ZRP	Zimbabwe Republic Police

Zimbabwe: Major urban centres

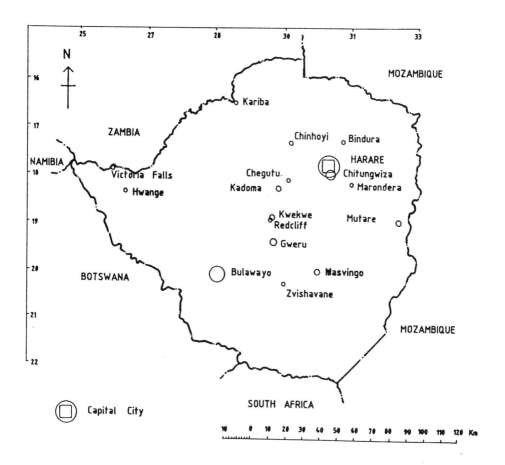

1 Introduction and Chapter Synopsis

Background and settings

Human settlements in Africa have never been identified or recognised at policy level as a key development sector for positive national development planning. Urban development has been given a 'backyard' position in National Development Plans vis a vis the rural sector. In some cases policies have been designed to discourage urbanisation.

This has continued despite historical evidence which demonstrates that urban settlements are the ultimate homes of the majority of peoples world over and are the engines for national economic growth. Rural to urban migration cannot be permanently reversed or halted; at most it can only be delayed. In addition there is also the fact that whatever sectoral policy/strategy adopted (industrial, agricultural, health, educational e.t.c), this will have a reference in space, content and operations. For each economic development process, there is an attendant settlement structure to go with it.

The neglect of urban areas seems to be thawing (at least in Zimbabwe) with more attention given now to the internal status of cities and their role in national development[1]. Human settlements are places were human beings live and conduct a wide range of social, cultural, economic and administrative activities for the sustenance of life. Critical in this regard is a perception of urban settlements as economic systems and ecosystems. Such a conception allows a definition and comprehension of production-consumption, production-reproduction attributes of settlements. These are a pivotal cog in the wheel that keeps national

1

economies going. The rural-urban linkages and the quality of the internal urban environment must be conducive to the promotion of national development.

With these perceptions of the urban settlement, we go in to tackle the specific socio-economic problems; one of which is the phenomenon of urban agriculture. It sounds a misnomer to talk of urban agriculture when the definition of urban is based on non-existence of agriculture.

In Eastern and Southern Africa, urban agriculture is a topic gaining increasing research, international aid and policy attention[2]. The starting point for recent works is the 'pioneer' study[3] done by the Mazingira Institute in 1985 which highlighted urban food production and the cooking fuel situation in urban Kenya[4]. Subsequent studies in Zambia, Uganda and Zimbabwe have been less extensive, but following the same themes in a more intensive manner. On the whole the research has focused on describing the phenomenon of urban agriculture and its importance for urban food production[5].

In many countries, the starting point has been that urban agriculture is an illegal activity. Therefore researchers have aimed to demonstrate its economic importance, particularly for the urban poor[6]. The official views have emphasised the environmental and health risks of urban agriculture, the violation of town planning zoning and used these as a basis to harass or prohibit urban cultivation. However the health views and environmental arguments against cultivation for example are based on conjecture rather than formal research insights. Ongoing research in Zimbabwe is now seeking to fill this gap.

Most researchers have aimed at informing the policy makers of the positive features of agriculture, giving accurate figures on productivity and improved self-sufficiency of households. They have highlighted the importance of urban agriculture as a survival strategy of the poor[7]. Again no serious attempt has been made to inform policy through participation of communities in the policy making process. This is yet another gap identified in Zimbabwe and to be filled by ongoing research.

In general, there are no outstanding results from science, technology and policy making for urban agriculture. Most research findings are of a baseline nature, telling us of the incidence of and actions in urban agriculture. For policy makers an important result is that urban agriculture cannot be dismissed as an illegal activity — it has become an integral part of the urban economy for both the poor and the rich[8]. Urban agriculture in African cities is widespread but in most cases it is subsistence agriculture with limited capital inputs and legitimacy to facilitate more intensive operations. Usually the scale is significant where the operators have legal access to land and therefore access to credit. In most African cities, urban agriculture is a transfer of rural subsistence agriculture to urban areas, particularly as whole families migrate and settle in urban areas.

Whereas the starting point for most researchers has been to inform policy makers of the existence and extent of urban agriculture, there is a need to contextualise the phenomenon within the overall context of urban economy. Firstly is urban agriculture a spontaneous activity? Should it be a planned activity, incorporated in the urban areas? Secondly, what are the consequences of making agriculture a major land use for the African city? Is it not better to make more 'efficient' use of the land by building more housing, industry or commerce? Thirdly, is urban agriculture an activity for the poor? Should it not be promoted and elevated in terms of self-sufficiency in food for urban centres (as in the case of Chinese and other Asian cities)? What would be the implications of all this on the urban poor and urban economy in terms of employment and local authority finance?

In Southern and Eastern Africa, urbanisation is a major process which will transform the economies by the turn of the century. Most urban centres were planned for much smaller populations and they lack adequate formal sector employment for the growing workforce. As a result most urban environments are characterised by informal sector activities, of which urban agriculture is increasingly an important feature.

The issues and questions which deserve future research in the southern and eastern Africa region include:

(a) rural — urban relationships and how they influence urban economic activity including agriculture. The rural urban migration trends and in particular the increasing urbanisation of families have to be properly contextualised. Most studies are very superficial and lack the framework in which urban agriculture is occurring. Understanding the rural urban dynamics will help in the understanding of the access to land , crop security and credit. Is urban agriculture simply a survival strategy or a response to economic opportunities?

(b) in countries where frameworks have been 'positive' about urban agriculture (Mozambique, Malawi and Lesotho), what have been the underlying policy reasons? How much is it a factor of land tenure and prevailing zoning systems or a product of interactions between traditional and modern land ownership forces? We have to ask again, should urban agriculture be a key urban activity? That it is found in all urban centres does not mean it should be promoted — we have to ask the reasons much more systematically.

(c) it is important to research urban agriculture not just from the perspective of the urban poor, but to examine a whole range of activities including capital intensive horticulture and dairying. There is a need for a typology or typologies which are inclusive of the phenomena as a whole. Far too often, the researchers focus on the peripheral/marginal urban agricultural activities simply to demonstrate that the poor are included. In Kenya, Zimbabwe and Tanzania, evidence suggests that high and middle income households constitute a significant proportion of urban agriculturalists. Marginalisation of the poor is increasing with inceasing collapse of the formal economic sectors on the continent[9].

The interrelations between agriculture, water, waste and disaster in the cities of the region are many and varied. With respect to urban agriculture's use of water, it is noted that in most cities of the region, urban agriculture is a seasonal activity following the annual cropping patterns. This also determines the types of crops and levels of intensity of cropping. Most urban cultivators, utilise 'vacant' pieces of land in the city, and there is no investment in water supply.

The middle and upper income groups operating on authorised land usually invest in boreholes or even small dams for certain size of landholding. In Harare, Zimbabwe and Nairobi, there are areas of the city which are zoned for small scale agriculture (horticulture, chicken production) where the original developers created boreholes and wells. In most cases the areas do not have reticulated water systems.

The use of waste water tends to be restricted in most centres although increasingly breakdown of sewers and water mains provide an opportunity for residents to tap on the supplies. In Harare, the Marimba and Mufakose areas are a good case where residents take advantage of breakdowns of the sewer mains and utilise sewage water to irrigate their maize plots. As will be detailed in a seperate chapter, cattle owners in Chitungwiza town 30 km south east of Harare take advantage of such incidents to irrigate pastures in the city. In Zimbabwe the municipalities have the monopoly use of waste water and treated sewage for 'municipal farms'. Evidence from the other cities does not suggest that urban residents have much access to the city's wastes. Most of the urban poor live in unserviced areas and therefore the disposal of wastes is not formally organised.

However, respect to agriculture and urban wastes, the interrelationships are not as clear cut in African cities as in the case in Asian cities. This is probably a legacy of peasant agriculture which tends to rely on animal and other organic manure, but does not utilise human wastes. Urban agriculture has therefore tended to follow the same established circles. The production nutrition systems tend to be

4

influenced by the lack of both capital and crop intensity. Entry points for further analysis of these issues are identified in this book. A reminder is also given that urban agriculture, particularly 'off plot peripheral' is fundamentally part of the urban system and has formed the basis of long standing European land use theory particularly that of von Thunen (1926)[10]

This book is based on research conducted in Zimbabwe since 1991. In a way, the research has rejuvenated local interest on urban agriculture. The research has so far confirmed the role of urban agriculture for household food supplies, employment of women and children and use of otherwise under utilised land. For the first time, evidence has been provided to show that urban agriculture does not benefit the poorest of the poor; indeed these have no access to the land as a result of both formal and informal gate — keeping processes in the city.

The work is also very significant in that it attempts to place urban agriculture within the context of urban economy, urban management and urban development. This is necessary if we have to provide planners with a more usable strategy. The gender dimension, environment, the institutional concerns and the quest to link urban agriculture to broader issues of housing supply and the fiscal base of local authorities are a significant new contribution of this work.

Chapter 2: Urban agriculture in Zimbabwe: issues and dimensions for research.

In this chapter the book outlines the nature of urban agriculture in the context of Zimbabwe accepting that the position of this activity is trivial in the urban and national context. It accepts the 'neglected' role and position of urban agriculture vis a vis urban management and planning. Then the questions for consideration are posed. Given the positive contribution to household economy, nutrition and food for urban families, why is it harassed or neglected?

The questions for research start here: a challenge to the poverty alleviation theme, a challenge to the 'institutional' apathy theme, a challenge to the purity of urban agriculture, a challenge to the essentialist argument which has been the rallying point of international agencies and proponents of the activity. In its current form it could be a development and environment cost, does not benefit the poor and does not assist in reversing the decay of urban economies.

These issues for research are presented in the form of a flow diagram. They are preceded by definitions of urban agriculture and a classification scheme based on legality and spatial dimensions of the activity.

Urban agriculture is an issue because there exist interpretation differences as to its value when considered in relation to the totality of urban management, economy and development. A review of experiences in Southern and Eastern Africa is given which illuminates the gaps in our knowledge — hence the policy responses which seem to misfire.

This chapter also gives a background of the research designs and data collection methods. The book is not based on one huge single study but on relatively small subject specific studies conducted over the years.

The methods of data collection are basically two. First were the qualitative methods designed to answer issues of policy, gender and decision making processes at the household level. To explore issues of policy, gender and environment, the research sought to promote/strengthen qualitative research methods. These include detailed interviews and discussions with cultivators and officials in the city council, participant observations and testimonies. Results and deliberations of chapters 7 and 8 are heavily dependent on these methods.

The quantitative methods of site sampling and questionnaire delivery were also utilized. Their limitations in this type of policy problem are highlighted in the chapters. Where appropriate each chapter makes reference to methods which were used for information collection and analysis. More work is still in progress to test new methods of monitoring urban land use especially through use of satellite images and computer technology as a substitute to air photographs.

Chapter 3: Aspects of off-plot cultivation in Harare: exploting the commons?

This chapter provides details on who the urban cultivators are, the crops grown, cropping patterns, reasons for taking up urban cultivation, length of stay in the city and use of outputs from the activity. It gives original materials from Harare which would be valuable for comparison wtih evidence from other cities. Such material will help answer question such as those posed elswehere, for example Rakodi (1985)[11]. A major departure in the chapter is the attention given to land issues within the context of rural-urban linkages, the aliens and a display of cultivation statistics from both the low income and high income residential areas. Further, a technical approach has been introduced to quantify and display plot sizes as well as laying a basis to pursue the question 'what is the ecological impact of cultivation in different physical environments?

6

Chapter 4: Urban cultivation on the 'home front' with special reference to space availability, utilization, equity and the environment.

In chapter two, the classification scheme spatially identifies on-plot and off-plot agriculture. In general the off-plot agriculture is the one which gives management problems at an urban level. This chapter calls for more attention towards on-plot agriculture. It attempts to link this with broader policy positions with respect to housing. Provision of housing continues to be one of the main problems confronting local authorities in Zimbabwe. Harare with a population of 1.2 million at 1993 has a conservative housing waiting list of 1 00 000 (one hundred thousand) household heads. The failure to provide housing is to a great extent related to the shrinking financial and resource base of the local authorities and the Zimbabwe national economy in general.

In response to this situation, researchers, international aid agencies and policy makers have experimented with a number of housing options targeted towards supply and demand variables. The methods of supply in general seek to reduce costs of provision. Reduction of standards (materials and space included) have taken the lead position in this regard. In theory such a reduction in standards will lead to a quantitative improvement in housing supply.

The objective of this chapter is to argue that in reality, reduction of housing standards in the Zimbabwe case militate against subsistence survival strategies of the urban poor (in the short run) and lead to reduced housing standards/conditions in the long run. Subsistence survival (by way of urban agriculture and home industries for example) is a significant sector for the urban poor given the decaying urban economies in Zimbabwe and more so the rest of Africa.

In the final analysis, it is cautioned that current policies on urban issues (such as housing) misfire due in part to a lack of a comprehensive analytical/theoretical framework which takes into account both spatial and non-spatial dynamics of urban development. Instead of just describing and documenting issues of urban subsistence, urban environments e.t.c a new thrust is needed with a focus on providing practitioners with a sustainable comprehensive framework for understanding and strategising on the issues.

But the chapter does more than this. It gives details of how space around the house is used throughout the year. Maize and vegetables are grown on the plots leaving no space for use as playground for the children. Consequently, children end up on the streets. Statistics are given to show how landlords monopolize both land on the home front and that on public open spaces. The equity issue comes up again. Even

7

more critical are revelations relating to positive use of organic wastes generated from cultivation on the home front. It seems possible that a more accurate estimation of the true population of urban cultivators can be obtained from approaches used in this chapter. An overwhelming view by residents is that urban cultivation should be promoted.

Chapter 5: Urban Maize Markets, Hammer Mills and the Urban Poor in Zimbabwe

This chapter tackes a number of questions previously raised. For exmaple the question of how to relate urban agriculture to other household economic, decison making and food procurement processes. The question by Rakodi (1985) on 'research into the effects of economic adjustment plicies on urban populations' is answered adequately in this chapter[12]. Covering the major urban areas in Zimbabwe, the chapter provides statistics and rationale for shifts in urban household consumption patterns away from expensive commercially produced to cheaper subsistence produced food. As in chapter 4 with respect to housing standards, IMF and World Bank brokered ideas on economic reforms are pushing people into poverty and subsistence survival. As a result, local comunities are drifting more and more away from their national governments. Like all other chapters in the book, the above issues are components of ongoing research work on which members from central government, the private sector and non-governmental organisations are involved.

Chapter 6: Institutional responses to urban agriculture; prohibitive or accommodative

This chapter starts from a historical and descriptive angle — tracing the nature and extent of urban agriculture in Harare over the past 15 years. There is a simultaneous and detailed documentation of responses by various institutions at local authority and central government level. Changing patterns in these responses are made evident.

The evidence (most of it from documentary sources) highlights that responses have been ranging from absolute harassment to passionate progressive accommodation. Harare City Council's response in the end is not as heavy handed as is generally alleged.

Why a sustainable strategy has failed to take root remains a major question. Here and elsewhere in the book, it is argued that cultivators have not honoured their part of the deal in the urban management game. This, coupled with lack of a solid conceptual/analytic framework to

8

inform policy are major stumbling blocks in the process of accommodating urban agriculture in Zimbabwe.

Chapter 7: Urban agriculture: testimonies of women from Warren Park

While the chapter has a gender dimension, it also reveals issues of management and destroys 'myths' built from previous researches. Blending with the gender issues implicit in chapter 8, it confirms the nutritional and economic value of urban agriculture at the household level.

But the poorest of the poor do not benefit. Infact these are excluded through formal and informal *gate keeping* practices in the sector. Issues of women landlordism are also brought to the fore.

Stability of urban residence or ownership of the residence and social networks are critical factors determining access to urban land for cultivation[13]. Hence the tenants and lodgers are excluded and as noted in chapter 3, a significant incidence of multiple plot ownership exists in the sector. Again the equity issue comes up.

Chapter 8: Images of urban agriculture; tools or products

This chapter follows up the issue of why interpretation differences exist on the issue of urban agriculture. It draws attention to how information is gathered, disseminated and used. It all depends in the eyes of the beholder. But eventually it is from these basic positions that fundamental policy decisions are made. The chapter is about techniques and concepts. The reader is made to participate in the process of image building and decision making. A series of images on urban agriculture are provided to assist in this regard. The chapter highlights the residual value of images.

After reading this chapter, the reader is likely to do two things: either go back and start all over again from chapter one or proceed with the rest of the book. There was a great urge to make this the first chapter of the book. But at chapter 8, in the middle, it rekindles the questions asked in chapter 1 and 2. It does so subtly and in a participatory way, thus providing the reader with the needed gusto to read the rest of the book.

Chapter 9: Subsistence urban cultivation in Zimbabwe; any lessons from the Europen allottment gardens?

This chapter opens up the topic of urban agriculture in southern Africa for comparison with experiences in Europe. So far, comparisons have been made with Latin America or Asian cities. Only marginal reference has ben made to European garden allottments experience in existing literature. Thus the chapter is a unique experiment which incidentally turns up historical material of relevance to our situation in Zimbabwe. It is designed to stand alone as a seperate article, and hence some paragraphs may seem repetitive with respect to overviews of the topic in Africa.

Urban economic decay in Zimbabwe and the rise of cultivation in towns seem to be lagging ten to fifteen years behind that in Kenya, Tnazania, Uganda and Zambia. This chapter shows that our experiences are a repetition of Europe fifty and one hundred years back. If that is the case, what are the differences and the lessons? Are we going to emerge victorious from this quagmire like Europe did, or are we condemend for ever?

Chapter 10: Urban agriculture as counterproductive and obstacle to urban development

This chapter is also a complete departure from the norm. Research outputs in Southern and Eastern Africa region glorify urban agriculture as an essential informal sector for survival and nutrition of the urban poor[14].

Having argued and revealed in previous chapters that the poor do not benefit from urban agriculture, this chapter presents evidence to support the view that in its subsistence form, urban agriculture has been a counter productive activity. It has been an obstacle which if measured in housing opportunities lost, is very significant. Never before has research focused on opportunity costs of urban agriculture. In this regard the chapter builds up on previous ones and sets interesting platforms for further research. Project planners and economists should find this provocative.

Chapter 11: Sewage effluent based urban agriculture in Harare: potentials, linkages and constraints

The reversal of urban economic delay is an issue of concern in Zimbabwe. If urban agriculture is to do this (contribute to the reversal), then it has to be upgraded from its subsistence position to a commercial position. This chapter reviews how the Harare City Council has utilized waste water from urban sewer systems to irrigate council farms. This resource is only available for the council and not to ordinary cultivators. However, if there is potential in this dimension we gain in two respects.

First in recycling of wastes and secondly in rejuvenating the urban economy plus supplying more food to urban residents from within the city. The chapter notes that commercialization would be very desirable but may not bring solace to proponents of the urban poor.

Chapter 12: The cattle of Chitungwiza, framing at cloe quarters or friction and conflicts on the rural urban fringe?

Urban agriculture in the form of cultivation is viewed as desirable by most urban residents in the country. The case is however different when it comes to livestock in towns. Cities have developed through displacement of rural people, first to make way for commercial farms then urban growth. In most cases, buffers of commercial crop lands and horticulture sound towns such that there is no daily interaction beteen rural subsistence community activities and the towns.

The case is different with Chitungwiza Town. Rural villages are close to the town and the peasant farmers graze their livestock on the town's open spaces; their former grazing land and homes. The case of Chitungwiza gives an opportunity to assess environmental and public health issues related to livestock in cities as well as use of sewage water in subsistence agricultural settings.

So far, urban residents do not appreciate the presence of cattle in the town and generally view this as problem. The chapter presents an outline of why this is the case and suggests that urban residents could probably change their views if they were to benefit directly from urban animal husbandry.

Chapter 13: Urban agriculture and urban development; the futures

In chapter 13, the questions are recast. We have covered ground in answering multiple questions. But more serious ones are still to be answered. The issues of revitalising urban economies are re-presented.

The chapter reviews a range of issues covered in the book and presents areas where research needs to be done. Most of these are clear and un-problematic. One of the objectives of this chapter is to urge researchers to develop an analytical and theoretical framework to inform urban management strategies. Such a conceptual analytic framework should take into cognisance the dynamics of urban development — which are sociological, political, economic and making themselves visible in a spatial-physical nature. When the dust has settled, when issues of data gathering and analysis no longer bother us, these substantive questions should be the pre-occupation of researchers in the region. The age of documentation is over.

Notes

1. For the first time, unlike previous national development plans since 1980, the Second Five Year National Development Plan (1991-1995) recognises urban development as one of the priorities.
2. So far IDRC Canada and UNDP seem to be the major funding agencies for urban agriculture research.
3. In Zimbabwe, there were studies before this in particular that by Mazambani D. (1982) which incidentally focused on the issues of peri-urban cultivation, wood fuel collection and energy in Harare; same themes in the Mazingira studies of 1985.
4. Mazingira Institute 1987, Urban Food Production and the Cooking Fuel Situation in Urban Kenya, Nairobi; Mazingira Institute.
5. While finalising the script for this book, other works on the same topic have been publicised. There was no opportunity to get these and incorporate them in the literature review.
    (a) Cities Feeding People: An Examination of Urban Agriculture in East Africa by Aumite Egziabher et.al (1994) IDRC, Ottawa.
    (b) Urban Agriculture ; Food, Jobs and Sustainable Cities, by Jac Smit et.al UNDP, New York (in press)
6. see Freeman D. B. (1991) *A City of Farmers: Informal Urban Agriculture in Open Spaces of Nairobi, Kenya.* McGill-Queen's University Press.
7. see also Maxwell D. and Zziwa S (1992) *Urban Farming in Africa; The Case of Kampala, Uganda.* ACTSPress, Nairobi
8. Consequently, serious policy shifts are needed to accommodate urban agriculture in Southern Africa. The importance and need for policy reflections are also well presented by Rogerson. see Rogerson C. M. *Urban Agriculture in Southern Africa: Policy Issues from the International experience.* Development Southern Africa, Volume 10 No. 1 February 1993.
9. Increase in poverty and collapse of the formal economy are critical conditions which push urban residents into urban cultivation. Hence the late entry or rise in the activity in Zimbabwe and South Africa - countries whose poverty levels were still relatively low compared to other countries in the region. Rogerson notes that the scale of urban agriculture in South Africa is still small . . .'is primarily a domain of the most marginalised and most vulnerable groups in urban areas, in particular elderly women'. This suggests non participation by middle class people in the activity and that better returns are still obtainable from putting the same land to alternative uses such as backyard shacks. It may be that urban middle income residents have not realised the potential of urban subsistence

cultivation. see Rogerson C. M. Urban Agriculture in South Africa, Scope, Issues and Potential *GeoJournal 30/1/1993 page 27.*

10. These have been used to explain intensive horticultural activities around cities even in Africa, but not the subsistence cultivation which is of interest here. For details see 'Von Thunen's Isolated State: An English Edition of Der Isoliete Staat by Johann H. von Thunen, translated by C. M. Wartenberg, edited by Peter Hall (1966) *Pergamon Press.* The theory is outlined in many standard urban geography texts; see for example Chapter 2 in Bradford M. G. and Kent W. A. (1977) Human Geography; Theories and their application. *Oxford University Press.*

11. Rakodi C. Self Reliance or Survival ? Food Production in African Cities With Particular Reference to Zambia. *African Studies, 21 (Spring 1985)*

12. Rakodi C. Self Reliance or Survival ? Food Production in African Cities With Particular Reference to Zambia. *African Studies, 21 (Spring 1985), page 61*

13. The importance of social networks for urban survival in Zimbabwe is outlined by Schlyter A. (1989) *Women Householders and Housing Strategies; The Case of Harare, Zimbabwe* (pages 186-189) The National Swedish Institute of Building Research

14. see especially Maxwell D. and Zziwa S. *(1992) Urban Farming in Africa; The Case of Kampala, Uganda,* ACTSPress, Nairobi

2 Urban Agriculture in Zimbabwe: Issues, Dimensions and Settings

1. Introduction

The question of urban agriculture in Zimbabwe has a trivial status; a position where it is viewed as insignificant. This is possibly a result of the minute contribution urban agriculture makes to national food stocks vis a vis the traditional and accepted zones of agricultural production i.e the rural areas (including commercial farms).

Urban agriculture is also viewed as "non-urban" ie it is not considered as a sector in a socio-economic sense as well as an active land use vis a vis other activities eg housing, recreation etc. This is understandable given the traditional conception and definition of urban as that which is non agricultural. In this regard it would be a misnomer to describe the activity in question as 'urban' agriculture.

Urban agriculture is the production of crops and/or livestock on land which is administratively and legally zoned for urban uses. This activity is done within these zones or at the periphery of urban areas ie land likely to be re-zoned from rural agriculture to urban land — the peri-urban areas.

Recently events have however indicated that our lukewarm stance towards urban agriculture is false and indeed unprogressive. At the tip of the iceberg is the issue of urban agriculture and urban land use planning for housing delivery[1]. A limited perusal of the literature and review of the phenomenon indicates more fundamental issues of concern for both the academic and urban manager.

a) What role does urban agriculture play in terms of incomes for the urban dwellers (urban poor)?

b) What role does it play in creating employment for women as an informal sector?

c) Is there any linkage between the phenomenon and the whole land question in the rural areas?

d) What have been the local authority responses and how sustainable are they?

Local authorities have to respond to the phenomenon basically because of the perceived environmental problems it may create plus the real land use conflicts it has generated. But because of the economic and gender dimensions that go with it, misplaced local authority responses can do more harm than good. On the other hand, can we afford urban agriculture in view of demands for urban land considering an urbanisation rate of 4.5 percent per year in Harare (or a housing waiting list of over eighty thousand families)?

The objective of this chapter is to identify the major issues for research and policy discussions and provide a framework for appreciating the discussions in the rest of the book. The discussion as a whole will seek to provide a framework for further research into urban agriculture by way of posing questions for detailed studies. This point is taken up again in the concluding chapter.

The definition of urban agriculture adopted for this work is designed to form a framework for the identification of linkages between the activity and the socio-spatial processes in the city. As noted earlier, it is the growing of crops or keeping of livestock on urban zones which town planners and urban managers have reserved for uses other than agriculture. Such designations are usually part and parcel of city development plans. Conventional land use designations on these plans are for; housing, industry, commerce, roads, railways, electricity servitudes or reservations, public services servitudes and recreation (golf, football pitches etc.), open spaces (ecological lungs)[2]. While town planners and urban managers have open space designations for future development or otherwise, the so called poor, view such land as idle land; an under-utilised scarce resource which could be put to immediate productive use such as agriculture.

2. Urban agriculture typologies

In this section an attempt will be made to provide a general classification of urban agriculture based on location and legality vis a vis responsible authorities as well as the product from the activity. Since the late 1970s some isolated work has been done on urban agriculture in the third world. While that on Africa has been patchy, studies in Asia and Latin America, have been more comprehensive. The point which emerges, for any late starter on the subject, is that parameters for a case study need to be clearly defined. Due to different agricultural and urban traditions there is some degree of divergence in our urban development processes, and the way these are managed. Zimbabwe for example has a well developed cadastral and land development system based on individual title — a feature very dilute in countries north of the Zambezi. As a result of this solid tradition Zimbabwe has the basis and reason to pursue a traditionalist urban management system comparable only to Europe, North America and Oceania.

Classification or the ordering of our experiences and perception of problems is therefore a necessity on the research process if we are to avoid the quagmire of disagreements and arguments of a semantic nature. Consequently the classification adopted here highlights the spatial, legal and production dimensions of urban agriculture in Zimbabwe.

In spatial terms in the Zimbabwean case there are clear divisions of urban agriculture (Figure 2.1). First there is that practised 'on plot'. On-plot agriculture is that which is done within the `pegged' residential stand. In Zimbabwe 95 percent of housing is on such land; one cannot start house construction until such surveying has been done and supporting infrastructure put in place. The plot owner can be identified in the Deeds Registry records as an individual. The majority of such cases are the residential stands on which the owner or his tenants will be found engaged in some form of agriculture.

In terms of urban management this form of agriculture is only problematic if the residents engage in livestock production, poultry e.t.c. With such activities nuisances generated are in the form of noise, smell and possible health hazards (Mosha 1991). On-plot crop cultivation is generally not viewed as offensive by the local authorities.

The other broader category is that to be labelled as off-plot agriculture where like on the 'on-plot' activity, crops and livestock production can be major activities. The difference is in the perception of ownership of land. Here land is perceived as to be 'public' land. Anybody can utilise it without anybody else claiming individual title ownership of the land e.g road reserves.

Urban Argiculture typologies

	ARABLE	NON-ARABLE
ON PLOT	Eg. - Maize - Vegetables - Flowers	Eg. - Goats - Rabbits - Poultry e.t.c.
OFF PLOT LEGALISED (With permit)	- Maize - Sweet Potatoes - Fruit Trees	- Sheep - Goats - Pigs - Poultry e.t.c.
OFF PLOT ILLEGAL (No-Permit)	- Maize - Sweet Potatoes	- Sheep - Goats - Pigs - Poultry e.t.c.

Problematic areas

Fig 2.1

Depending on circumstances, off plot agriculture can be legal or illegal. It is legal if the agriculturalists have a permit from the local authorities and vice versa if they do not have. Although the bulk of discussions will be biased towards off-plot agriculture, there is a great deal of on-plot urban agriculture in Zimbabwe.

3. Urban agriculture in Zimbabwe: Harare vs other African cities

How prevalent and significant is the issue of urban agriculture in Southern Africa? Is the issue of urban agriculture not unique to Zimbabwe? The pioneering study in Zimbabwe, Mazambani (1982) looked at the activity of urban agriculture, wood-fuel collection and energy in the city of Harare. These were seen to create rural landscapes within the urban environment; sometimes described as ruralisation of urban areas. Coverage of African cities in that study unfortunately cited west African experiences. Although the activity is also very prevalent there, these cities have a different historical development and different morphological outlook compared to Harare and cities of Southern Africa in general. This point has merit when one attempts to distil a theory of urban agriculture which is circumscribed by a general theory of urban development.

In Kenya (The Mazingira Study), it is reported that twenty nine percent of urban households grow crops in town, seventeen percent keep livestock in town and that United States seventeen million dollars worth of livestock were kept in Kenyan towns at 1985 (Lee-Smith 1991 p. 3) In Lilongwe, Malawi, goats are a prevalent feature in towns. The growing of trees is promoted and the trees are latter used for fuel by urban residents (personal observations and discussions with officials October 1991, July 1994)

Freeman (1992) also working on Nairobi utilised and extended the Mazingira studies. The focus was on the spatial distribution, the practices, the motives of cultivators and the problems faced by cultivators in urban Nairobi. The value of urban agriculture products for low income households was again emphatically documented

Rakodi (1987) reported similar occurrences for cities in Zambia and drew parallels with Indian cities where cows are prevalent in the cities. In a more detailed study, Sanyal (1987) highlights the financial and economic value of urban agriculture to the urban poor in Zambia dismissing both the modernisation and neo-classical theories propagated against urban agriculture. Also from Zambia in an earlier period were studies of a medical nature Watts et.al (1978) focusing on the link between mosquito breeding (and hence malaria) and flora typologies in the city. It was scientifically observed that mosquito breeding on maize plants or any other crops is not significantly different from that on other plants growing naturally.

Work has also been done in Tanzania in the 1980s[3]. Major objectives were to investigate the nature and origin of food production activities within the urban centres and their peripheries. Six towns: Dar es Salaam, Morogoro, Dodoma, Mbeya, Kilosa and Makumbako were surveyed. In these centres, local authorities were reported to have 'initiated' some form of structures to accommodate urban agriculture. The poor were identified as needing a more positive environment to engage in urban agriculture; including such resources as more access to land and credit.

The town of Maseru, capital of Lesotho is even more diverse in its urban agriculture. Dairy cows, maize cultivation, sheep and pig rearing, vegetable and fruit production are dominant and conspicuous activities (personal observations and discussions with officials December 1991 and October 1993).

In view of the above observations, a few salient features need comment vis a vis the situation in Zimbabwe.

Alienation of urban agriculture

In addition to being considered illegal those involved in off-plot urban agriculture are subject to sporadic harassment by urban local authorities (Kenya & Zimbabwe). Maseru is unique in that it takes an enabling approach where urban agriculture is accommodated and supported. The town provides special veterinary services through the Ministry of Agriculture's Livestock Division (Working Paper No. 9, 1990 p. 27)

Urban agriculture and the urban poor

In all cases, it is noted that urban agriculture is an important sector in the urban economies particularly for the urban low income families, women and children. In Maseru, the estimates available indicate a value of urban agricultural production to be six million seven hundred and five thousand maloti at 1990; One maloti = One South African Rand (Working Paper No.9 1990).

Urban vs rural agriculture

Studies in Kenya and Lesotho point to higher yields per unit area for urban agriculture when compared to rural rain fed grain production which may have existed before urbanisation of the areas. The implication is that urbanisation does not necessarily mean the end of agricultural production. African cities in the pre colonial era are seen to have taken

20

urban agriculture as part of the urban way of life. Rakodi (1987) underlines this point and indicates that at a latter stage, some colonial governments did promote the activity.

In summary therefore, the issue of urban agriculture is common in most cities in Africa. The differences seen in the different countries are in magnitude, typologies and more important the institutional responses. Responses can be either prohibitive or accommodative/ enabling. That of Zimbabwe seems to fall in the prohibitive category.

4. Urban agriculture: issues and dimensions

The question we may ask is: "Why and how is urban agriculture an issue? " On Figure 2.2 an attempt has been made to display the major dimensions of research and policy importance on this matter. It is an issue basically because there exist interpretation differences as to its value when considered by urban managers vis a vis the urban poor and other stake holders. How much do we know of this activity and how remote is a compromise response to the phenomenon? Urban agriculture boosts the assets base of the urban poor and reduces vulnerability of women and children to urban economic collapse. To mothers who are providers of food in the home, urban agriculture provides them with a varied range of nutritious foods which would be beyond their means if obtained from the open market. Observations and discussions with cultivators in Zimbabwe reveal that for at least two months, an urban family can meet its mealie-meal requirements from off plot urban agriculture produce.

In terms of governance, Harare has a repressive urban management approach divergent from current enabling urban management approaches world wide and scornful of the needs of the urban poor. The whole subject is a challenge. It is a challenge to current urban land use planning and urban research to come up with more accommodating approaches. Though studies have been carried out on the subject, it is clear that they have homogenised the urban poor in general and urban cultivators in particular. Yet it is clear that women dominate the urban informal sector especially urban agriculture. The gender bias in urban agriculture needs not just acknowledgement. Like the class character of urban poverty, it needs detailed study and analysis to influence approaches in dealing with the poorest of the poor in the urban areas. Subsequent chapters will however demonstrate that the poorest of the poor in urban areas are excluded from urban agriculture.

The preceding section has attempted to provide a framework for research on gender issues in the context of urban agriculture and economic survival of the urban poor. The premise for doing this is that

21

Figure 2.2
Urban agriculture — issues and dimensions

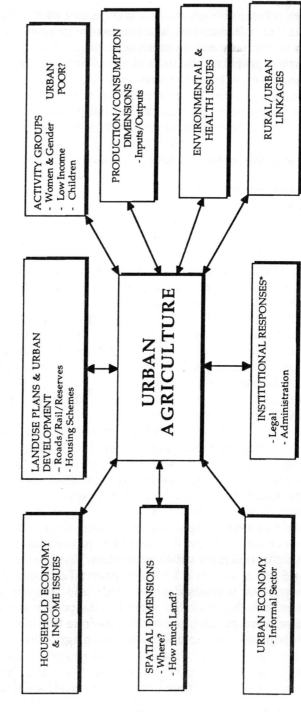

* Including logal Govt. public participation, representation and community groups

for gender work to be less rhetoric and receive an increased hearing, particularly to policy makers who are mostly men, its linkages to the rest of the other daily human problems must be displayed.

The starting point for most researches so far has been to inform policy makers of the existence and extent of urban agriculture. Proponents have used essentialist arguments to call for recognition of urban agriculture without providing indicators of how this should be done.

There is a need to contextualize the phenomenon within the context of urban economies beyond the household level. Can urban agriculture contribute to the reversal of urban economic decay in African cities? Should it be a planned activity incorporated in the urban areas? What are the institutional and economic consequences of making agriculture a major urban land use? Is it not better to make more use of the land by building more housing, industry and commerce? Does it really benefit the poor and can it be used as another strategy to raise food self-sufficiency in urban areas? What are the environmental implications of urban agriculture? Antagonists purport that the activity is a health hazard, promotes land degradation, pollution, destruction of urban habitats and siltation of reservoirs. To what extent are these allegations supported by evidence and what is the contribution of urban agriculture relative to that of other urban processes such as construction, industry and so on.

This book will not provide answers to all these questions. We have to agree on whether there is merit in pursuing them and if so, in what ways. We also have to consider other matters not cited here but relevant to the research topic.

5. Research designs and study areas

In this section a brief outline will be given of the research designs and study areas for field surveys conducted mainly in Harare the capital city. The research designs follow from the questions raised in preceding sections, the urban agriculture typologies identified earlier and spatial practical realities in the urban areas. In order to capture city wide processes, data and information is needed from all major categories of land use, S_{11} to S_{23} on Table 2.1 To these six study sectors, we have to add a seventh, the peri-urban agriculture. This will not be dealt with in this presentation though some work has also been initiated in the sector. The presentation on methods will be limited to those sectors were detailed work has been done so far.

Table 2.1
Urban agriculture study areas in Harare

Urban land use zone

		Low Density Residential	High Density Residential	Industiral & Other Areas
Urban Agriculture Space Typologies	On Plot	Mandara ◒ Mt. Pleasant ◒ Vianona ⊖ S_{11}	Warren Park ● S_{12}	Rugare O Willowale O S_{13}
	Off Plot	Mandara ● Mt. Pleasant ● Vainona ● S_{21}	Mufakose ⊖ Warren Park ◒ Mabvuku ● S_{22}	Rugare ⊖ Willowvale ⊖ S_{13}

Legend	●	=	Covered in detail
	⊖	=	Used for pilot studies
	◒	=	Partially covered
	O	=	Still to be covered

In spatial terms, for Harare, the sectors or zones in these sectors can be identified on the Map 2.1. High density residential areas are former 'African locations' of colonial days. They house up to 75% of urban populations. Property sizes are on average 300m². Since 1992, with pressure from the World Bank and USAID, the standard has been reduced to 150m². At present there is significant overcrowding due to housing shortages in the city[4]. The low density residential areas are the formerly "Whites only residential areas" of colonial days. Properties here are on average above 4000m². Although racial labels have been removed, upper class citizens (indigenous included) inhabit the low density areas while the lower class citizens inhabit the high density areas[5].

Map 2
Urban cultivation in Harare: Location of study areas

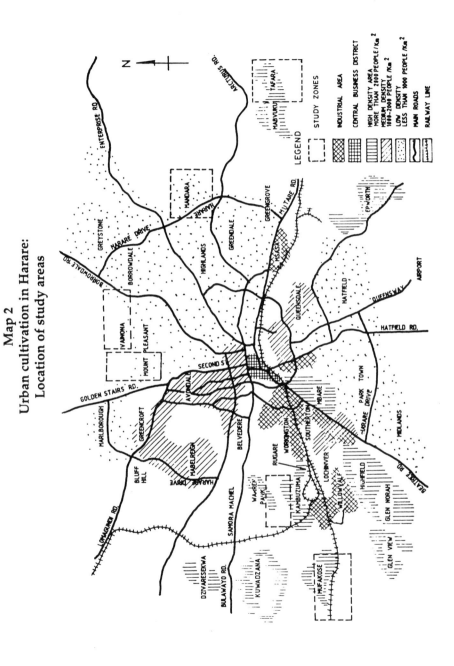

On-plot cultivation

Activities in Sector S_{11}, that is on-plot cultivation in low density areas, are yet to be covered in detail in a systematic approach. So far only physical checks to determine space under cultivation have been done. Some illustrative photographs and base maps are also available.

In Sector S_{12}, that is on-plot cultivation in high density areas, the survey used structured questionnaire surveys, interview type, delivered in 1993 and 1994. Questions sought to record details on whether families were involved in off-plot cultivation, if so when, where and the participants involved. This can be an indirect way of approximating the population of off-plot cultivators in a given area[6]. It also recorded the existence of on-plot cultivation, the types of crops grown, the space available, other non-agricultural uses of the space and the status of house development. Cadastral details on properties were obtained from the department of the Surveyor General and the City Council. Some details on this sector are in the chapter on cultivation on the home front.

Sector S_{13} focusing on on-plot agriculture for industrial zones has also not been covered in detail. In this sector, aspects of interest would include cultivator profiles and health aspects of the crop outputs given the industrial pollution in the zones. Significant technical and financial support is needed for this sector and the study is likely to be pursued in partnership with local industrialists who are concerned with atmospheric pollution in the city.

Off-plot cultivation

Urban cultivation covers almost all areas in the cities, namely open spaces in high density, low density, residential and industrial areas, roads and railway reserves. Ideally, the objective is to select a sample representative of each category of broad land uses. The main constraint would be resources to cover all these strata.

At the sampled area level, the problem is to get a reasonable sample of cultivators to work with. There are problems in that there is no known population of cultivators to sample from. Secondly the plots they cultivate are neither uniform nor well delimited. At times communal type cultivation is practised. Thirdly there is no period during which one can find all households or cultivators on the plots at the same time.

For Sector S_{21} two sites were selected in Mandara and one each in Vainona and Mt. Pleasant (see Map 2.1). These were sites where significant cultivation was taking place at the time. Structured questionnaires were delivered to cultivators identified on the plots at any time during the survey period. A total fifty five cultivators were successfully interviewed on these sites in 1993.

For Sector S_{22} that is off-plot agriculture in high density areas, the surveys were conducted in Warren Park (late 1992) and Mabvuku/Tafara (1993)[7]. Details from the former are documented in the chapter on testimonies of women from Warren Park while those from the latter are part of the chapter on off-plot cultivation. Mufakose and the Rugare/ Willowale industrial areas were also covered under this sector. Although no questionnaire surveys were conducted here, field visits and discussions with council officials concentrated on these areas as will be apparent from the chapter on institutional responses to urban agriculture in Harare.

Surveys using questionnaires were also conducted in Chitungwiza on health aspects and conflicts arising from cattle in the town. In addition to these surveys, extensive desk evaluations of office reports and files notably from Harare, Chitungwiza, Bindura and Glendale towns were also a good source of information. The surveys on maize marketing and milling covered Bulawayo, the second largest city in Zimbabwe. Field visits and discussions with city officials were also held in Sheffield. Photographs were collected from archives or new ones taken in all towns. In addition workshops, seminars and conference discussions were very helpful in developing some of the materials contained in this book[8].

Notes

1. Pursued in the chapter on institutional responses and that on images of urban agriculture.
2. Pursued as a separate component of on-going research.
3. IDRC Sponsored Research (1983) on Urban Agriculture Research in Tanzania.
4. For details on this subject, see among others, Mutambirwa and Potts (1991)
5. Aspects of post independence (1980) intra-urban migrations in Harare are available in Cumming (1993) chapter 13 in Zinyama *et al Harare, The Growth and Problems of the City,* University of Zimbabwe Publications, Mabelreign Green-Ways and Drive In Cinema, Local Development Plan No. 20, City of Harare, Department of Works, Planning Division, May 1993.
6. Studies on urban agriculture so far have failed to come up with an objective method to determine the population of off-plot cultivators on a seasonal basis.
7. Mabvuku will represent Mabvuku-Tafara areas

8. Such workshops include: a) Gruphel Workshops, 30th March-2nd April 1992 and 2nd-3rd   March 1993.

   b) **RUPSEA** conferences, October 1991, Lilongwe, Malawi and October 1993, Maseru, Lesotho.

   c) 10 th Inter-Schools Conference On Development, 29-30 th March, The Bartlett School of Graduate Studies, University College London.

   d) Urban Agriculture In Zimbabwe, One Day Seminar, 24 th July 1993, University of Zimbabwe, Harare.

   c) Regional Development Planning Occasional Seminar, Friday, 1st October 1993, ISS, The Hague, The Netherlands.

3 Aspects of Off-plot Cultivation in Harare: Exploiting the Commons

1. Introduction

This chapter presents an overview of off-plot urban cultivation based on 1993 field surveys conducted in Mabvuku/Tafara high density area, and sites in Vainona, Mandara and Mt. Pleasant low density areas of Harare. Using two student assistants, surveys were carried out in February at a time when cultivators were engaged in late planting and weeding of their plots. The surveys sought to establish plot sizes, crops grown, cropping patterns, inputs, outputs and decision making and awareness of local authority regulations regarding cultivation on open spaces in the city. Examples of sites in low density areas are given on Maps 3.1 and 3.2 highlighting the existence of large continuous tracts of land reserved for future development or otherwise.

A total of ninety seven valid questionnaires were obtained from these surveys with a distribution by area as shown on Table 3.1 A total 43 percent respondents were from the high density areas. This grouping of low density versus high density will be referred to in the text where appropriate.

Map 3.1
Stand 148, Lot 3A of Mandara, Harare
Reserved soccer recreational field converted to maize cultivation

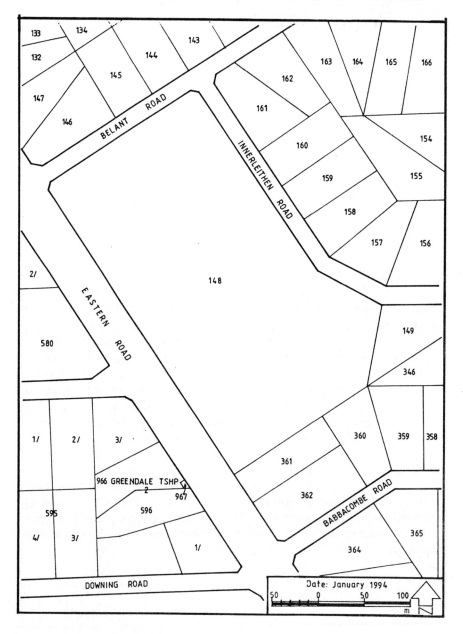

Map 3.2
Subdivision The Grange, Mandara, Harare
Reserved for future housing development

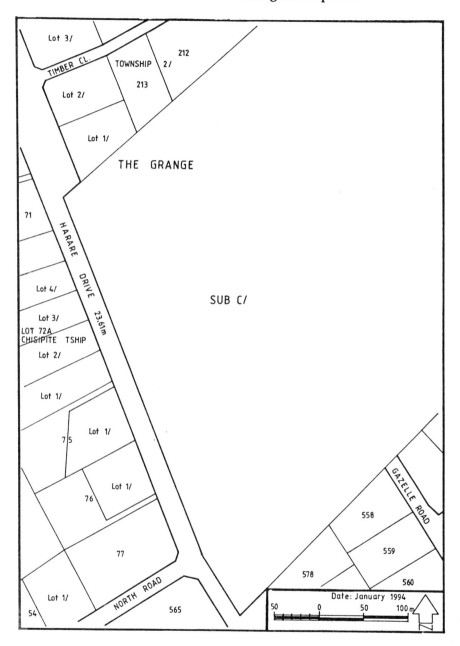

31

Table 3.1
Distribution of valid off-plot questionnaires by study areas

Study areas or site	As % of total
Mabvuku — Tafara	43.3
Mandara (2 sites)	25.8
Mount Pleasant	17.5
Vainona	13.4
Total	100

(n = 97)

Source: January 1993 surveys

2.   Overview of results and findings

Legality aspects of off-Plot cultivation

Using the urban agriculture typology adopted in Chapter 2, Table 3.2 shows the prevalent off-plot type of agriculture by legality and modal split at the time of surveys.

Table 3.2
Legality aspects of cultivation by area in Harare, 1993

		% in all areas	% in low density areas	% in high density areas
	Legal	37	7	76
Type of	Arable			
Agriculture	Illegal	63	93	24
	Arable			

Generally cultivators in the low density areas (93 percent) had no permits whereas in high density areas, up to 76 percent of cultivators

32

had at some stage in the past obtained permission to cultivate on the current sites. This could be explained in terms of the co-operative effort promoted in the mid 1980s which was more accepted in high density areas than in the low density areas. Those recording 'legal cultivation' in Mabvuku could be remnants from that era. It is also clear that a significant number of people now do not have permits. The survey did not demand proof of permit from those respondents who claimed they had one.

Perception of 'legality' based on previous permission has been analyzed against the years spent cultivating the current plot in the Mabvuku area. The distinction between legal and illegal is now distorted by the fact that some cultivators who previously had permits have continued to cultivate without going back to renew these permits (a later section will come back to the issue and explore the extent to which the cultivators are aware of council policy on urban cultivation)

Agricultural activities on the plots

In almost eighty percent of all cases at the time of survey, maize was the crop grown on the plots; alone or in combination with some other crops. Other crops included beans, pumpkins and sweet potatoes. At the time of the survey, cultivators had completed planting and were in most cases weeding. Spraying of fertilizers was not prevalent at this time although respondents indicated that they do use fertilizers. In a parallel survey 14 percent was established as the proportion of cultivators using inorganic fertilizers on such plots[1].

Plot sizes and zoning

The plots cultivated were/are lands reserved for future development or are recreational land, undevelopable land (dambo areas) or land at the edges of existing development which is yet to be planned for built development. The sizes of the plots varied from small plots of 200 m^2 to as large as 9,000 m^2. These estimates could be on the high side since no actual measurements were taken. Approximations were done by the research assistants both of whom were students of town planning and familiar with distance approximations. However there is a chance that different individuals cannot give the same approximations in all cases.

Secondly, the respondents's information on the extent of their plots could be inaccurate at times especially where an individual plot was part of a co-operative plot. Unless the assistant suspected this situation and made the question very clear, errors could arise with cultivators giving co-operative plot sizes for individual recordings[2]. It has been noted that there are much higher plot sizes in the low density areas than the high density areas. Co-operative plots size per capita are also much higher than the other categories.

Work is ongoing on terrain characteristics of cultivated areas with interest on plot sizes, informal tenure systems, soil quality, slope and degradation potential. As part of this work, accurate tacheometric surveys are a key exercise. Map 3.3 is a product of such an exercise conducted in Kuwadzana high density area located west of Harare city centre. Plot sizes, materials used to mark boundaries and slope of sites are highlighted.

Cultivators use stones or earth embankments to delimit plot extent. At the time of the survey (October 1994), there was very little vegetation cover on the plots making such areas highly susceptible to erosion especially with the first thunderstorms which come in October/ November of every year. Plot sizes vary and are in the range established using elementary estimation methods described earlier. On the same map, a big plot of 3 150m^2 had been ploughed by tractor in readiness for the new planting season. Further north of the area, the slopes are quite steep (1:7). These are the areas we need to protect from uncontrolled cultivation. An emphatic position on the potential environmental damage requires information on rainfall intensity and soil characteristics. While this is a desirable set of statistics, limited resources have stalled progress in quantifying cultivation impacts on soils and water bodies. Hopefully, the material will be part of a future publication.

Inputs into urban cultivation

Inputs were mainly in the form of seeds purchased from local shops, from the city centre or stored from the previous season's harvest. An attempt was made to get information on costs and quantities, but in the majority of cases, these were difficult to obtain. With no records kept, such information would be a bit unreliable. One could estimate from the areas covered by crop the amount of seed that could have gone down at planting.

Implements are in the form of hoes *(badzas)*, shovels and tins. Unlike in Warren Park, none of the respondents in these areas mentioned any use of hired tractors for tilling of the land although council as well as private tractors have been available for hire in all areas including Tafara and Mabvuku[3]. Although human labour is an input in all cases some respondents did not bring this up when requested to itemise the inputs into their activities.

Map 3.3
Terrain features of cultivated plots:
Kuwadzana maize fields, Harare

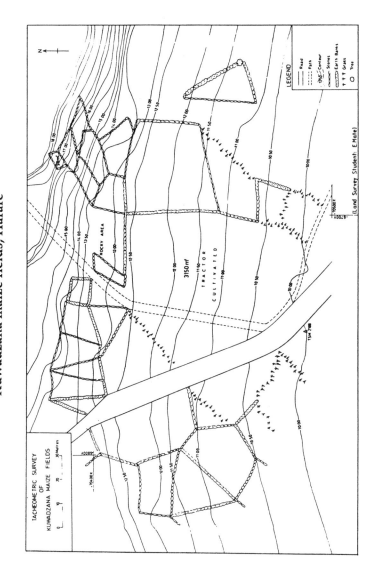

Output from urban cultivation

Output is closely related to crops grown. This chapter is using pre-harvest material and so will not have details of quantities produced. However even at that early stage, respondents were asked to indicate how they intended to use their produce or how they had used the produce from the last season. The major use of output is home consumption of the fresh produce or use during the year as mealie meal (for the grains). Selling of output for cash and for use as fodder (especially chicken feed) were also noted in a number of instances. These are aspects which need further study since they have more extensive linkages with other activities in the city. In general, eighty percent of output is for own consumption while fresh or dried. The average yield per acre was estimated to be 7 bags of maize representing 4 months supply of maize-meal for a family of seven members[4].

Plot patronage

At the start of every season, cultivators should form co-operatives and get registered with the local authority in order to get a plot allocation and permission to cultivate. This hardly happens nowadays. In this situation, what is the rate of entry of new cultivators in the sector? What conditions force people in the activity despite the constraints to plot availability and the possible harassment by the city council including slashing of the crop?

The average years cultivating a plot was 3.6 years for all respondents. This was slightly higher in the high density areas (3.85 years) and lower in the low density areas (3.4 years). In general 62 percent of the cultivators had been cultivating on their plots for 3 years and less i.e 62 percent of the cultivators entered the sector within the three years, 1990, 1991, 1992. Therefore a significant proportion of urban residents entered the cultivation industry in the 1990s; the years of drought and economic structural adjustments.

In the high density areas, the proportion of those cultivating for more than five years was only 5 percent. It is not possible to quantify the relation between increase in the number of cultivators and the actual area under cultivation. From air photo analysis, the area under cultivation in 1993–94 was about double that under cultivation in 1990. Approximately 5 thousand hectares of land was cultivated in 1990 compared to about nine thousand hectares in 1993; representing between 15 and 20 percent of the city's total area. Possibilities are that subdivision of existing plots takes place to accommodate new entrants into the sector. A detailed year by year monitoring and plot audit using air photographs or images from remote sensing and field visits could assist in getting an accurate picture in this regard.

One can however safely conclude that the growth of numbers entering this sector is correlated with the incidence of the 1991-92 drought and the harsh economic climate in the country related to the IMF/World Bank sponsored economic reform programme generally known as Economic Structural Adjustment Programme (ESAP) whose implementation coincided with increased unemployment in the country and general decrease in the purchasing power of residents.

Continued cultivation of a plot is also affected by the respondent's residence in an area. For a resident who is a lodger and whose tenure is unpredictable and changes quite often, this may disrupt continued cultivation on a given plot. The average years of residence on the same premises was 8,2 years in the low density areas where the majority of cultivators were domestic workers housed on premises of their employers. In high density areas, the average was 16.8 years. This average is exceptionally high and is due to the proportion of the cultivators who own the residence on which they live. Ownership of a house in the high density areas seems to be a major condition for engaging in off-plot cultivation.

Cultivation of more than one plot

A significant proportion, about 26 percent of the respondents, cultivated more than one plot in the same or other area. This feature was more associated with older residents in the city especially those who had no household member in full-time formal employment. Those residents with multiple plots had at least 5 years in the city and resident on current premises at 1993.

Spatial aspects of plot utilisation and residence of cultivators

Before coming to the residences they currently occupied, cultivators originated from a wide range of places as shown on Table 3.3.

37

Table 3.3
Location of previous cultivator residences

Place of origin	% of cultivators
Same area	13.7
Surrounding farming areas	9.5
High density + Chitungwiza	27.4
Low density areas	28.4
Other outside Harare	20.0
None of the above	1.1
Total	100

(N = 97)

About 70 percent of the cultivators had relocated from an urban home in their last move and not from the rural areas. Therefore urban cultivators are not necessarily recent immigrants from rural areas.

Ownership of places of residence

In general the cultivators from Mabvuku owned the residences on which they live (or members of their households did own those properties) compared to cultivators from the low density areas who were dominantly domestic workers housed in the servants' quarters on premises of their employers.

The survey made efforts to establish the distances people perceived they travelled from residences to their plots (one way trip). At a later stage this could be compared with the map distance between the plot and the cultivator residences. The main interest here is just to establish how close the perceptions of the ordinary citizen is to reality.

In the high density area of Mabvuku, the mean distance was 1.77 km while in the low density areas the mean was 1.75 km. From the cultivators' perceived distances, we can conclude that the distance travelled by cultivators to their plots was on average within 2 km from their places of residence. In general 92 percent of the cultivators lived within 5 km of the plots they were found cultivating. For those cultivators who were employed as domestic workers in the low density areas, this implies that they could afford to use tea and lunch breaks to rush to their plots, do some work and then quickly rush back to work. They could also afford to do some work on their plots after formal working hours. The bulk of them used these periods to cultivate. In terms of research design, the best times to find cultivators on the plots during mid-week are: early in the morning before 8.00 am, during lunch hour from 1 to 2 pm and in the evening after 4.30 p.m. However given the limited time cultivators have, especially soon after the first rains, they may find activities of researchers intrusive and delaying their work.

Participation status and decision making profiles

Urban cultivation is perceived to be a part-time activity. In general, cultivators were female (63 percent). Of the females interviewed, 51 percent were involved in the activity on a full-time basis while the proportion of men for the similar category was 33 percent. A significant proportion of cultivators were involved in this activity almost on a full-time basis at the planting and weeding stages.

Generally, cultivators tendered their own plots (88 percent of the cases). The remaining 12 percent respondents interviewed were cultivating as contract labourers. Only one female was found in this category ie. as a contract labourer. The contract labourers are employed by plot "owners" to perform tasks such as digging and weeding. This was consistent with findings from elsewhere in Harare and other areas where relatively well to do women employed men to do manual labour on their plots.

Although adoption of cultivation as a survival strategy is made by women, in almost all cases they have to obtain the blessing of their husbands before proceeding (in the case of married women). Some significant differences existed when it came to decision making on use of cultivation outputs. About 80 percent of women respondents indicated that they or their female elderly made these decisions (Table 3.4).

Table 3.4
Decision making on use of cultivation outputs; women cultivators

Who makes decisions on Use of output	% of Total
Women cultivator (Self)	68.4
Women (not respondent)	15.8
Joint (husband & wife)	5.3
Male relation of respondent	10.5

(n = 57)

In general therefore, women are in control of what they produce. As noted in the survey most of the output goes for family consumption. Given the need to keep the family surviving, the women may have constraints in the options to which they use their outputs. Instead of using output for their own direct or individual benefit, they use it for the family benefit. One may argue that women have no choice but are forced by circumstances to use cultivation outputs for family benefit.

How do the cultivators obtain their plots?

By law, a resident intending to use a piece of land for urban cultivation should get permission from the local authority through the Department of Housing and Community Services. This Department works closely with the Department of Works (Town Planning, Land Surveys) and The Town Clerk (Municipal Police Unit, Legal Section). The survey established that in the 1993 season, the majority of cultivators did not follow this procedure in obtaining plots. They simply went in and started using the land. Informal networks were used to co-ordinate and regulate plot sizes and entry into the sector within any given locality. By sex, a significant number of women went ahead to cultivate without using council channels.

It is clear from the returns that all cultivators in the low density areas had not utilised facilities of the local authority irrespective of sex. Cultivators revealed however that they had some awareness of council by-laws on the issue (Table 3.5) and that the major sources of information on this aspect were the radios and general discussions with colleagues.

Table 3.5
Awareness of council policy on cultivation by area

	Low density areas	High density areas	Total	%
Aware	51	29	80	83
Not Aware	4	12	16	17
Total	55	41	96	100

(N = 96)

The survey also made an attempt to establish whether there was any linkage between urban cultivation and shortage of land in rural Zimbabwe. The bulk of the cultivators (69 percent) were found to be without rural land. For those with land, there were a number of scenarios on how they used that land. Some of the respondents made periodic visits to their rural homes to cultivate. Others had families or relatives cultivating the land.

For those without land in the rural areas, it was established that the bulk (55 percent) were of non-Zimbabwean origin (Table 3.6). Malawians dominate this group (37 percent) followed by Mozambiqueans (15 percent).

The prevalence of non-Zimbabwe cultivators can be explained in historical terms with respect to labour migration in Southern Africa and laws regulating access to land in Zimbabwe's rural communal lands. These laws make it difficult for foreigners to own land. Historically, Malawians constituted a significant proportion of the urban labour force in Zimbabwe especially in mining and domestic work. They were more permanent urban residents than the local black Zimbabweans who migrated to their rural homes periodically. For a long time, indigenous black Zimbabweans had no permanency in the towns and their families were dominantly rural.

Although the trends are changing with more black Zimbabweans assuming urban permanency, the majority have rural homes from where they can obtain supplies of farm foods. The high incidence of Mozambiqueans could be a post 1980 era when a lot of them fled war in their country to more peaceful Zimbabwe. Most of them have survived through informal activities. They are also a source of cheap labour for those who need domestic workers (this is illegal in Zimbabwe for security reasons but difficult to monitor). Some of the residents, especially where inter-marriages have taken place, considered themselves to be more Zimbabweans than foreigners.

Table 3.6
Reasons for no rural plot by area

| | Study areas | | |
	Low density	High density	Total
Foreigner (Mozambiquean)	0	10	10
Foreigner (Malawian)	11	14	25
Foreigner (other)	1	1	2
Land shortage	7	2	9
Prefer urban home	2	0	2
Other	13	6	19
Total	34	33	67

3. Concluding remarks

The typology and issues arising from chapter 2 were used as a basis for the study elaborated on in this chapter. The results confirm current thinking on the subject as well as give new insights that could be useful to research in cities other than those in Zimbabwe. It confirms the dominance of women in off-plot agriculture. Using a poverty definition based on access to formal employment, house ownership (a significant asset), women headed households and recent urban immigrants, evidence from this chapter supports the view that the beneficiaries of urban cultivation are not in the category of the urban poorest. Indeed, some well to do urban residents take this activity as a commercial venture. From this observation, a question that arises for proponents of 'affirmative action' on urban agriculture is 'what entry point to use; poverty alleviation or profit maximisation?'

There are also issues which need further review such as internal dynamics of plot ownership, access to plots, gate-keeping mechanisms and multiple plots ownership. The implied collapse of the 'co-operatives' has only been briefly discussed and would need further elaboration in a separate article on institutional responses to the phenomenon.

The bulk of the output from urban cultivation is for domestic consumption while fresh. Maize is also used for meal-meal at a later stage during the course of the year. Most of the women cultivators are responsible for making decisions on how to utilize the output from the cultivation. This shows again that women do contribute to economic sustenance of developing countries in ways not captured by national accounting techniques in practice.

Respondents in the surveys were seen to be cultivating plots quite close to where they lived. In the low density areas, most cultivators were domestic workers and lived in units provided by their employers while in the high density areas, the proportion of domestic workers was smaller. The bulk of cultivators from high density areas were unemployed but they or a member of their family did own the houses in which they lived.

A significant number of off-plot cultivators were of Malawi and Mozambique origin, a factor which militates against their access to rural land. Cultivators of Zimbabwe nationality cited land shortage in their rural homes. This is a matter which needs further review to establish whether respondents in this category would be willing to take up agriculture in resettlement areas if the land were made available.

The tough economic climate especially since 1990, seems to be the driving force behind urban cultivation. Cultivation is seen as a significant source of food in the home; releasing pressure on the family budget. Cultivation is thus a contrarian industry i.e. it is on the increase when the formal economy shrinks as is the case in Zimbabwe since 1987. Despite an awareness of the city council's legal policy on urban cultivation, cultivators irrespective of sex, ignore the procedures and cultivate when and where they see fit. Implications of this on environmental degradation and urban management are matters to be pursued in separate chapters.

Notes

1. Mudimu and Chigume (1993 pp 5) Paper 4, Urban Agriculture in Zimbabwe, One Day Seminar, Dept. of Rural and Urban Planning University of Zimbabwe.
2. This possible source of error had not been anticipated. Neither had it been picked in pilot surveys. Any future work would have to make the questionnaires explicit on the matter.
3. The 1994–95 planting season has seen more council tractors made available for this purpose in Tafara/Mabvuku
4. Mudimu and Chigume (1993 pp 5) Paper 4, Urban Agriculture in Zimbabwe, One Day Seminar, Department of Rural and Urban Planning, University of Zimbabwe.

4 Urban Cultivation on the "Home Front": With Special Reference to Space Availability, Utilisation, Equity and the Environment

On - Plot Cultivation in Zimbabwe: Emerging issues

Affordability and sustainability

On - plot cultivation is dependent on the availability of space on each individual property. Residents on any property have automatic access to the space for uses such as cultivation. The issue becomes one of whether the spaces are large enough for such uses especially now that standards for housing space have been reduced from 300m² to 150m² for low income residential areas.

Secondly where lodgers share the same property with the land-lords (subsistence landlordism), the landlord may not make land available to the lodgers. This raises the issue of equity in terms of whether the poorer households have access to on-plot land for survival activities. In the same vein if on-plot cultivation takes an upper hand as a domestic space use there may be no space left for other needs such as children's playing area, washing lines etc.

Thirdly availability of space will determine options for handling wastes arising from whatever cultivation on plot there is. Blatantly, on

45

plot cultivation raises questions on the sustainability of residential areas in a situation where space standards have been reduced.

What is the population of cultivators in cities?

Quantification is a basic issue which comes up in any debate on urban affairs. For urban cultivation, two questions that arise relate to the hectarage of urban space under cultivation as well as the proportion of urban residents engaged in the activity. Both quantities vary annually. The space quantity can be established by mapping, air photograph analysis or satellite image analysis where these exist.

But still the population is difficult to get for off-plot cultivation. As noted elsewhere in the book, off-plot cultivators are never in the fields at the same time. In the case of Zimbabwe, the activity is highly informal with no system of monitoring. A possible way to get the population of off-plot cultivators is to target urban residents on their properties. In January 1993 such an approach was used and established that 20% of residents in Harare's High Density areas were off-plot cultivators. This could have been an under estimation of the cultivators because in an environment where the activity is seen as illegal, residents may have found it appropriate to identify themselves as non off-plot cultivators at a time when they were planting crops. There was a need to pursue the same issues at harvesting time when the illegality factor would not impact negatively on the residents.

Study objectives, study area and study designs

Objectives

The objectives of this study of on-plot agriculture were:

a) to determine whether use of on-plot surveys can be a basis for establishing the population of off-plot cultivators in Harare.

b) to establish the amount of space potentially available for cultivation. This is the non-sealed surface on any property and was estimated from the sealed surface factor.

c) establish current practice in terms of access to land and equity.

d) establish potential inadequacy of on-plot space for various uses including children's playing space.

e) establish levels of population density in the area.

f) establish current practices in handling wastes from cultivation with respect to maize stalks.

46

g) provide other information useful for urban management and understanding of cultivation in particular.

h) obtain tentative attitudes of residents towards urban cultivation and establish whether sex and tenure affect views on the issue.

Study area: homogeneity vs heterogeneity

The Study area, Warren Park 1 residential area, Harare, was established soon after independence as a housing scheme meant for the low income residents (Map 4). The local authority provided wet cores (maximum of two rooms and a toilet) which recipients would develop within specified periods. Currently 90% of these properties are fully developed 3 to 4 bedroom houses. Stand sizes vary from 250m² to 400m². The larger properties of 400m² form a buffer on the northern limits of the area along Bulawayo Road. In total there are about 3420 properties (excluding Warren Park D). Unfortunately Warren Park 1 is only a segment of a larger census enumeration unit making it difficult to get the official Central Statistical Office (CSO) population size for the area. The local authority and district housing office estimates that the area has a population of 40 000 people. In spatial terms, there are clearly identifiable zones bounded by local distributor roads.

Although the area is labelled as a high density low income area, a significant number of the properties are now occupied by high income households. This has happened through two processes. First is the upward economic graduation of some of the original residents. Second is the downward infiltration and invasion by middle income households who have found it difficult to purchase or rent houses in the high income sector properties. Despite original government policy prohibiting selling of houses at market prices in schemes targeted for the low income, the higher income groups have invaded some of the recently established low-income estates renting houses or purchasing properties outright. Warren Park is one area where this phenomenon has been observed[1]. This has happened on larger properties along the Bulawayo road. Resident households on these properties are a mixture of owners, tenants or lodgers. The lodger phenomenon is a result of both housing shortage and related overcrowding and subsistence landlordism[2].

Therefore the study area is not very homogenous as implied by the term high density low income area. There are categories by property size, fabric, tenure and socio-economic standing of resident households. A research designed in high density areas should therefore aim to capture these differences.

A total of 310 respondents answered the survey questions. On each property the eldest persons were invited to respond to the questionnaire.

Map 4.1
Warren Park high density area, survey zones and blocks

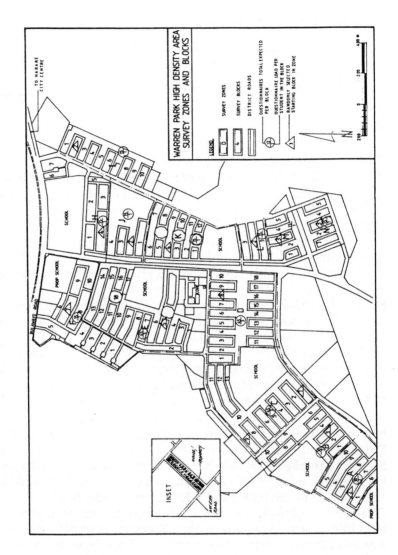

There was no deliberate effort to target groups in the population (lodgers, women or the poor). Although desirable, the expense was beyond our capacity in terms of material, financial resources as well as time. However these groups were still captured in the survey returns.

Survey revelations: space matters

Socio-economic profile of respondents

The total sample of 310 respondents was composed of 45.5% males and 54.5% females. This trend of more females than males was dominant in the lower age groups. For age groups above 41, there were generally more male respondents; a deviation from normal population distribution by sex. However this feature is with respect to 15% of the sample and no efforts were made to seek an explanation for it. Table 4.1 provides a summary of the age sex structure of the sampled population.

About 24% of the respondents were lodgers or belonged to lodger families while 70% were owners or belonged to owner families. The remainder were tenants or other type of residents not fitting in the owner or lodger category. The lodger proportion in reality is much higher than reflected here. Where a lodger and owner happened to be present during the survey, the lodger would always give the landlord (owner) the platform to respond to the questions asked. It would be considered disrespectful and a breach of protocol for a lodger to respond to the interview in the presence of his/her landlord. Problems have been recorded where lodgers ignored this protocol. For example the owner of the house would interject each time questions relating to lodger status on the property were asked. Such a development is likely to affect future relationships between lodger and owner. In the survey, efforts were made to minimise such situations. However, it would be of great academic merit to target lodger respondents separately from the owner category. One hopes that those lodgers captured in the survey as executed, provided representative responses. Table 4.2 provides a picture of the tenure and sex status of the respondents. In terms of residence on the properties, the majority (63.2%) had been resident on the same properties for 10 years and above. This feature of long duration is skewed in favour of owner respondents as depicted on Table 4.3. Attention should be paid to the shaded cells on this table.

The majority of lodgers (66%) have been on current properties for 5 years and below. In effect, the mean number of years on current property for lodgers is 5.44 years with a standard deviation of 4.66 years. The mode is 1 year and median is just below 3 years. This is an indication that lodgers could be quite mobile. Other studies could explore reasons for this mobility in detail. The distributional patterns of lodgers per property, population per property, infants and children per property seems to be uniform throughout the area. There are minor differences between study zones. We should however note that zone H which has larger properties generally had larger numbers of population and lodgers per property (see Table 4.4). This data was graphed as block and whisker plots and the differences between zones were seen as insignificant. The differences between zone H and the rest of the area are more apparent if the figures on Table 6 are considered in terms of space availability per capita. For statistical enthusiasts, the figures can be used to proceed to do analysis of variance tests (ANOVA). The results are however not likely to yield different conclusions from the ones already noted here. Therefore in spatial and physical terms, the area is broadly homogenous except for zone H. Socially, there are significant social groupings according to tenure, sex, age and economic status.

Table 4.1
Age sex structure of respondents (%)

Age	Males	Females	Total
11-15	1	2	3
16-20	7	9	16
21-25	9	10	19
26-30	5	8	12
31-35	4	8	12
36-40	7	12	19
41-45	4	3	7
46-50	4	2	6
51+	5	2	7

(n = 310)

Table 4.2
Sex and tenure status of respondents %

	Lodgers	Owners	Tenure Tenants	Other	Total
Females	16	35	2	1	54
Males	8	34	2	3	46
	23	69	4	4	100

(n = 310)

The level of none responses

Although in total 310 valid questionnaires were recorded, one finds that responses to some of the questions on a questionnaire could be missing or not considered valid. No efforts have been made to quantify such situations but where results are tabulated, the n value below each table if less than 310 could be a result of some questionnaires excluded from analysis due to points noted above. The survey's concern directly focused on non-responses on properties. A brief explanation could assist. On obtaining a successful interview, say on property 28, the survey assistant was supposed to record any properties skipped before getting to property 28 as a result of refusal to answer questions or absence of residents on the preceding properties. In total 31 (thirty one) non-responses were recorded constituting close to 10% when compared to successful interviews at first approach. Table 4.5 gives a summary of this comparative situation.

Of the 10% non-responses, 60% were due to residents refusing to answer questions while the remainder was due to complete absence of residents on the properties or absence of residents senior enough to answer survey questions (11 years and above). Those refusing to answer questions, did not want to be bothered or were not satisfied with some aspect(s) of the survey. Some lodgers felt they could not answer questions without their landlords' knowledge in case the latter returned during the interview exercise. Although no serious effort was made to explore these refusals the reasons for such refusals could be pursued as part of other studies especially where the proportion increases. For this survey, the objective was simply to record such non-responses for use as a bench mark in future surveys.

Table 4.3
Length of stay on current property by tenure of respondent

		Lodger	Owner	Tenant	Other	Total
Y	1	20	5	2	0	27
E						
A	2	7	7	0	2	16
R						
S	3	12	5	2	0	19
S	4	3	6	1	1	11
P						
E	5	6	5	2	0	13
N						
T	6	1	5	0	0	6
O	7	2	4	0	0	6
N						
	8	1	9	0	0	10
C						
U	9	0	4	0	0	4
R						
R	10	1	16	2	0	19
E						
N	11	5	13	0	1	19
T						
	12	6	59	0	3	68
P						
L	13	6	56	2	0	64
O						
T	14	3	14	0	1	18
	15	0	3	0	1	4
Total		73	211	11	9	304

n = 304

Table 4.4
Inter zone differences

Plot Population

Survey block	A	B	C	D	E	F	H	I	J	K	L	M	N
Sample size	30	28	47	41	46	14	15	15	15	15	13	16	14
Sum	270	278	417	414	461	146	186	111	160	155	139	142	138
Mean	9	9.93	8.87	10.1	10.02	10.45	12.4	7.4	10.67	10.33	10.69	8.8	9.86
Standard deviation	3.6	3.27	2.16	3.53	4.41	5.17	5.44	2.16	3.74	3.06	4.37	3.26	1.56

Plot Population (Lodgers)

urvey block	A	B	C	D	E	F	H	I	J	K	L	M	N
Sample size	30	28	47	41	46	14	15	15	15	15	13	16	13
Sum	64	57	96	89	128	46	97	11	48	34	54	30	29
Mean	2.13	2.04	2.04	2.17	2.78	3.29	6.47	0.73	3.2	2.27	4.15	1.88	2.23
Standard deviation	1.94	1.9	1.67	2.3	3.15	4.86	7.09	1.39	3.41	1.58	3.08	1.5	0.83

Plot Population (Children)

urvey block	A	B	C	D	E	F	H	I	J	K	L	M	N
Sample size	30	28	47	41	46	14	15	15	15	15	13	16	14
Sum	38	42	70	59	81	28	28	25	27	22	34	23	17
Mean	1.27	1.5	1.49	1.44	1.76	2	1.87	1.67	1.8	1.47	2.62	1.44	1.21
Standard deviation	1.48	1.26	1.33	1.21	1.39	1.8	1.41	1.11	1.08	1.92	1.85	0.96	0.8

Plot Population (Infants)

Survey block	A	B	C	D	E	F	H	I	J	K	L	M	N
Sample size	30	28	47	41	46	14	15	15	15	15	13	16	14
Sum	34	45	63	57	67	22	47	0.8	22	14	21	20	21
Mean	1.13	1.61	1.34	1.39	1.46	1.57	3.13	0.8	1.47	0.93	1.62	1.25	1.5
Standard deviation	0.97	2.25	1.11	1.12	1.19	1.34	5.08	0.77	0.74	0.88	1.19	1.18	0.85

Table 4.5
Table 4.5
Survey non-response levels

Non response level	Frequency %	Cumm. %
0	89.9	89.9
1	8.8	98.7
2	0.3	99.0
3	1.0	100.0
Total	100.0	

Population on properties and space Adequacy

On average the plot sizes are 252.10m² (two hundred and fifty two square meters). The mode is 200m² (63% of properties) while only 12% of the properties are about 400m² (four hundred square metres). Therefore, although pre 1992 design policy stipulated a minimum of 300m² (three hundred square metres) stand/property sizes for low income areas, significant areas already had stand sizes of below that minimum. For Warren Park 1, 82% of properties have sizes below 300m².

These sizes become more meaningful when combined with population on properties. On average the population per plot is 10 people with ranges as high as 23. Only 25% of properties had no lodgers at the time of survey. On average there are 3.39 lodgers per property with further distributional details as given on Fig 4.1 below. One to three lodgers on a property seems to be the norm in Warren Park 1.

Space adequacy can be assessed from a review of the open space available (non-sealed surface) relative to population of those who need such space for example infants and children. Infants for example are still too young and vulnerable to use public open spaces. In most cases due to space in-adequacy on properties, children utilize the roads as playgrounds. This is coupled by non-availability of formal public playgrounds.

On average, 75% of the residential property is sealed; usually occupied by the house itself. In some cases, car garages (for overnight safe parking), tuck shops, and backyard shacks take up the space. Taking a property size of 200m² (prevalent in Warren Park) and an infant and child population of 4 (four) per property obtained in the survey (for

Figure 4.1
Lodger counts on Properties in Warren Park 1, 1994

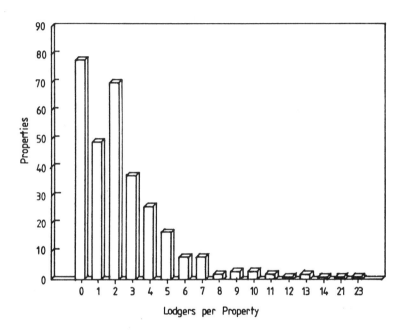

80% of properties) we could compute the space available per child in the area for use as playing space.

Property size	=	200m²	(A)
Non sealed surface factor	=	25%	(B)
Infants + children	=	4	(C)

$$\text{Space per child of 10 years and below} = \frac{A * B}{C} = 50/4m^2$$

$$= 12.5m^2$$

For property size of 250m², this figure rises to 16m²/child. When we consider that the child competes for this space against other uses such as gardening, car park pace etc, then this space is grossly inadequate. Such a position is tenable when we include the fact that at any point in time 80% of properties have vegetables or maize growing on the spaces (summer reason) and 60% (for winter season). This partly explains why we have many children on the streets in Zimbabwe.

Uses, access and adequacy of on-plot space

On plot non-sealed space is used for a variety of activities which include gardening, playing space, recreational space, laundry space and space for other production activities such as chicken raising, welding, car repairs, tuck shops etc. Gardening is a prevalent activity which uses such space. In the rainy reason maize growing also dominates and was recorded as present to varying degrees on at least 84% of the properties.

Relative to their needs, residents find the on-plot space inadequate as given on the Figure 4.2. This level of inadequacy is not affected by tenure status nor by sex of respondents. Whether lodgers, owners, males or female, respondents viewed the space as inadequate to very inadequate as given on Table 4.6(a) and 4.6(b). We have to acknowledge that the survey data did not reveal much by way of how space adequacy perception is affected by age and economic status.

Do lodgers have access to on-plot space for gardening?

In terms of equity, not only did the survey consider space availability for children but lodgers as well. In economic terms, lodgers pay rentals which are used to upgrade the houses as well as sustaining the owner/ landlord. Despite their significant role as income suppliers to the landlord, lodgers generally have low access to on-plot cultivation land. Of the 229 properties where lodger presence was reported, only 31% of

Figure 4.2
Views on residential space adequacy,
Warren Park 1, 1994

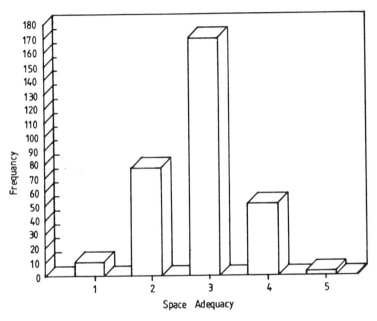

Space Adequacy

(n = 310)

1 = Very Adequate

2 = Adequate

3 = Not Adequate

4 = Very Inadequate

5 = Can't Say

Table 4.6(a)
Space in-adequacy by tenure status of respondent

	Lodger	Owner	Tenure Tenant	Other	Total
Very adequate	3	5	2	0	10
Adequate	18	55	0	4	77
Not adequate	38	117	9	5	169
Very inadequate	14	37	0	0	51
Can't say	1	1	0	0	2
Total	74	215	11	9	309

Table 4.6(b)
Space in-adequacy by sex of respondent

		space adequacy				
	Very Adequeate	Adequate	Not Adequate	Very Inadequeate	Can't Say	Total
S Female	4	37	100	25	2	168
E						
X Male	6	40	69	26	0	140
Total	10	77	169	51	2	308

these lodgers were reported as having access to on-plot space for gardening (see Table 4.7).

In most cases, the reason for lodgers having no access to garden space was that, the available space was too small for any of it to be spared to the lodgers. Some landlords alleged that lodgers have no interest in gardening. This could well be true since, tenancy of lodgers in the long-term is not guaranteed. Considering that the period of stay on a given property is uncertain, it would be rational not to invest any significant sweat on the property. Hence the lodger may not use the on-plot space for gardening even if that space were available.

Table 4.7(a)
Access of lodgers to on-plot garden space
properties with lodgers

	Frequency	%	Cumm.%
Have Access	71	31.0	31.0
No Access	158	69.0	100.0
Total	229	100.0	100.0

Table 4.7(b)
Do lodgers have access to on-plot garden space?
responses by tenure status of respondent

		Tenure status of respondent				
		Lodger	Owner	Tenant	Other	Total
Access To	Positive	30	38	2	1	71
Land For	Negative	42	107	5	4	158
Lodgers	Total	72	145	7	5	229

(n = 229)

Table 4.7(c)
Reasons why lodgers have no access to
on-plot garden space

	Not enough space	Not interested	No response	Other	Total
No Access	122	7	10	5	144
	122	7	10	5	144

The level of space inadequacy is also reflected by the respondents' views on how much space planners should provide for future houses. Over 77 % of the respondents recorded that future houses should have more space than what they currently have. These are views from residents with some form of shelter (lodgers and owners). The responses could be in the opposite direction if we targeted the same questions to squatters in order to get a broad picture of preferences. However lodgers are people without houses of their own. The fact that they too prefer bigger plots may be an indication that we should start providing houses according to the needs of the people without necessarily pursuing a policy of 'owner occupied accommodation'. In other words, there is need to revisit and revise the current government policy that families should own the houses that they live in. This existing policy should be weighed against making housing available, provided by whoever can afford to and make it available for renting. Implicitly, it is a call to officially extend the markets for housing into the so-called low income housing sector.

The tables 4.8(a) and 4.8(b) further illustrate the point that even lodgers who don't own houses would wish to be allocated larger properties than those currently available in Warren Park 1. Due to the overcrowding in existing housing stocks, and the insecurity of tenure that lodgers have, one could view them (lodgers) as legalised squatters in Zimbabwe.

Do lodgers have access to space for off-plot cultivation?

In pursuance of the equity issue the survey considered the degree to which lodgers have access to off-plot land for cultivation. A total 42.2% respondents reported that they engaged in off-plot cultivation during the 1993/1994 cultivation season. Only 7.8% of that 42.2% were lodger respondents. Another question was asked to all respondents on whether lodgers resident cultivated off-plot. On 229 properties where lodger presence was recorded, 46.3% of lodgers were recorded as cultivating off-plot. When compared to the total population in Warren Park 1 the proportion of lodgers cultivating off-plot is quite low. Lodgers have to compete for off-plot space with landlords. Again uncertainties as to tenure on a given property does militate against engaging in off-plot cultivation.

Table 4.8(a)
Preferences on property sizes for future housing
compared to current properties (all respondents)

Desired property	Frequency percent	Cumulative %
Same as this	16.5	16.5
Larger than this	77.4	93.9
Smaller than this	4.4	98.3
Other	1.7	100.0
Total	100.0	100.0

(n = 310)

Table 4.8(b)
Preferences on property sizes for future housing
compared to current properties (lodger respondents)

Desired property	Frequency percent	Cumulative %
Same as this	19.7	19.7
Larger than this	70.4	90.1
Smaller than this	8.5	98.6
Other	1.4	100.0
Total	100.0	100.0

(n = 310)

What is the population of off-plot cultivators?

It has been noted that the population of urban off-plot cultivators is difficult to establish from off-plot based surveys. From property based surveys, forty two percent of the respondents recorded that they were off-plot cultivators in the 1993-94 cultivating season. This figure is almost double the estimate obtained in early 1993 for the same area using similar survey methods. We can confirm that a significant number of residents engage in off-plot cultivation. If the 1993 estimate was accurate, then there has been a hundred percent increase in the number of off-plot cultivators in Warren Park. The final figure of forty two percent is about

61

6 percent lower than that obtained in the pilot survey when thirty nine respondents were sampled. This survey confirms that it is indeed possible, quite feasible and accurate to estimate the population of off-plot cultivators using on-plot based surveys.

Promotion of urban agriculture: do residents support it?

The question on whether residents support promotion of urban cultivation is relevant in at least two respects. Initially we need to gauge urban residents' views against those of the urban managers. The latter are generally antagonistic to cultivation in urban areas. Then there is also a new wave of urban cultivation protagonists spearheaded by western social scientists and non-governmental organisations who wish to be associated with survival strategies of the poor especially those affected by economic structural adjustment programmes sweeping across Africa. If any meaningful urban cultivation projects are to be launched, the support of the residents will be crucial. Hence their needs and basic views on this issue have to be assessed.

The mood of respondents is that urban agriculture should be promoted. This is the view held by sixty three percent of the respondents while another 12 percent would only promote the activity subject to conditions. These latter residents would like to see urban cultivation accompanied by better provision of housing, services and protection of urban land against degradation. The diagram (Figure 4.3) and the accompanying Tables 4.9(a) and 4.9(b) capture the views from a numerical angle. Sex of the respondents and tenure status seem not to have any effect on the perception of respondents towards promotion of urban cultivation.

How do residents manage organic wastes from on-plot cultivation?

One key entry for proponents of urban agriculture projects is that of promoting organic farming and environmentally friendly ways of handling wastes. For example, maize stalks can be handled in a variety of ways. Stalks could be destroyed by burning or just left on the plots to be blown away by the winds or to decay. Maize stalks can also be collected and dumped on open spaces within the neighbourhood. In such cases, environmental nuisances are created. Burning creates smoky environments which are not palatable in a highly populated area. The health risks have so far not been assessed. Dumping or neglect of stalks creates solid wastes which have to be removed by municipal refuse and amenities teams. This at the expense of all residents irrespective of

Figure 4.3
Respondents' views on promotion of urban cultivation,
Warren Park 1, 1994

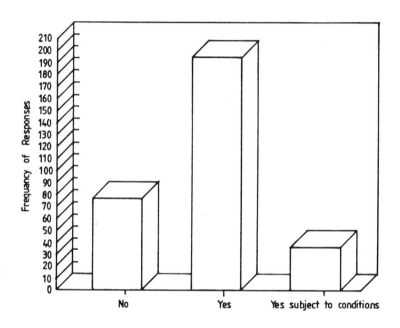

(n = 310)

Table 4.9(a)
Should urban cultivation be promoted?
responses by sex of member

		Sex		
		Female	Male	Total
Should urban	No	38	38	76
cultivation	Yes	111	83	194
be promoted ?	Yes s.t.c	18	19	37
	Total	167	140	307

s.t.c   = subject to conditions

Table 4.9 (b)
Should urban cultivation be promoted?
responses by tenure status

		Tenure				
		Lodger	Owner	Tenant	Other	Total
Should urban	No	21	48	4	3	76
cultivation	Yes	46	139	5	5	195
be promoted?	Yes s.t.c	7	27	2	1	37
	Total	74	214	11	9	308

s.t.c   = subject to conditions

whether they cultivate or not. This raises questions of equity and 'free riders' in utilization of urban environments. The environmentally friendly approaches include composting of the maize stalks to create manure which can be used as fertilizer in the coming season. This way, use of unfriendly inorganic fertilizers is minimized.

For those respondents who had maize crops on their plots during the 1993–94 season, about eighty-eight percent had harvested their crop by the time of the survey. Maize cropping is done once a year in the majority of cases. Vegetables are then grown for the rest of the year. Respondents had used or intended to use various methods to handle or dispose of the maize stalks. The majority use either pit or surface compost to handle the stalks. Only fourteen percent of the cultivators burn the stalks while another 2 percent dump stalks on public neighbourhood open spaces.

The above figures show us that residents are to a large extent already aware and are practising environmentally friendly methods of handling wastes arising from cultivation activities on-plot. Use of composting methods requires a significant amount of non-sealed surface on the properties. During the period that the compost is maturing, some land which could be used as playing space for children or for year round vegetable growing is forgone. Again this is an illustration that the on-plot space given to high density residents is fully utilised. Hence most of them would prefer to have larger spaces for their properties than currently provided.

Concluding remarks

Use of urban space for agricultural activities has not been seriously considered in urban development dialogues despite the fact that output from "informal" urban agricultural activities contributes significantly to the survival of the urban poor. Recognition and planning for cultivation activities in cities requires that we understand more on how the activity currently operates. The chapter has tried to shed more light on how residential space is utilized for urban agriculture with special focus on space availability, access by status of residents and implications of this use on space standards, environment and urban sustainability.

In addition to pursuing the said research objectives, the study was used as a teaching exercise for a group of fifteen second year planning students. The study revealed that although high density communities are not homogenous, accurate results can be obtained by taking small samples randomly selected from the larger area.

Details and information on sub-groups in the communities (e.g. women only, or lodgers only) were obtained from the survey. In future studies these groups could be targeted separately although doing so would prove quite expensive. More females than males and more owners than lodgers were part of the sample captured in the study. Due to security of tenure which is not guaranteed, lodgers stay an average 5 years (median) on a property before moving to a new one while owner residents stay longer on one property (average 10 years).

The study has shown that while lodgers contribute to the economic survival of their landlords, they are excluded from significant use of home space and have to compete against land lords for off-plot space. In general, the residential space available is too small for the needs of residents. Survival production activities dominated by cultivation and vegetable growing, use the bulk of the non-sealed surface home space. Consequently recreational space especially for infants and children is non-existent. As a result, children use road space as playing space where they compete against traffic and other public space users. Residential densities for low income people have been made higher and higher. It seems this is being done at the expense of residents' space needs for subsistence survival and recreation.

Despite the space inadequacy residents make maximum use of it, even parcelling out portions for use as compost space. A question for the future is whether residents in the low density areas are using their space intensively as well. Only a minute fraction of residents burn the organic wastes from urban agriculture while the majority make compost for manure used in the next season as fertilizer. Thus residents are to a large extent more environmentally responsible than is at times thought.

It is interesting to note that irrespective of residential status or sex, residents encourage the promotion of urban cultivation activities.

This revelation is crucial as a starting point for those designing urban agriculture projects where the residents are to be involved.

Notes

1. Mutizwa-Mangiza N.D. and Rakodi C. (1989) Housing Policy, Production and Consumption, A Case Study of Harare. RUP Teaching Paper No.3, Dept. of Rural & Urban Planning, University of Zimbabwe.
2. For details, see Kumar S. (1992) Subsistence Landlords and Petty Capitalism: A Theoretical Framework For The Analysis of The Production and Exchange Of Low Income Housing In Third World Cities. Working Paper Number 58, Development Planning Unit, University College London, The Bartlett.

5 Urban Maize Markets, Hammer Mills and the Urban Poor in Zimbabwe[1]

M. Chisvo, W. O. Goromonzi and L. Munro[2]

I. The economic and policy settings

A lot of reference has been made and will be made to urban agriculture as a phenomenon arising from tough economic conditions in Zimbabwe in the 1990s. This chapter seeks to provide some details related to that hypothesis with special reference to informal maize milling in urban areas and consumption by the poor. Although the original research work was done in the context of assessing impacts of ESAP and food needs of the poor, the findings highlight linkages between economic policies, household consumption of maize meal[3] and cultivation in urban areas. The chapter indicates possibilities for situating urban agriculture within the framework of urban economies and urban food security.

In 1991, the Government of Zimbabwe embarked on a five year Economic Reform Programme, generally known as ESAP, to redress both internal and external imbalances that exist in the economy. As part of this reform programme, government also liberalised the maize market. For example, on 1 June 1993 the Government removed the subsidy on roller meal and at the same time liberalised the regulation of maize marketing. In October and November 1993 the Ministry of Public Service, Labour and Social Welfare (MPSLSW), in collaboration with UNICEF, conducted a maize market study in the four largest cities, Harare (including Epworth), Bulawayo, Chitungwiza and Mutare, to ascertain the impact of these reforms on urban food security.

This chapter presents findings of that study in summary form. Special emphasis was placed on studying the hammer milling industry and its customers, since strong anecdotal evidence and the preliminary results of other studies suggested that poor urban consumers were turning to straight-run maize meal *"mugayiwa"* milled by hammer millers after the removal of the subsidy increased the price of roller meal by roughly 50 percent in June 1993. The results of this study suggest that hammer millers can supply over half of urban maize meal demand with straight-run maize at prices comparable to or even lower than the old subsidised roller meal price. Furthermore, the hammer milling industry is expanding rapidly, especially since the reforms of June 1993, and will be able to satisfy an even larger portion of the urban maize meal market in the near future.

2. Sampling and study methods

The hammer mills were identified and located using a sampling procedure known as "snowball sampling". This technique is suitable for sampling when the size, composition, and/or location of the members of the population under study are unknown at the start of the research project. Essentially, snowball sampling involves finding one or more members of the population, interviewing them, asking them to identify other members of the population whom they know about, then tracking down and interviewing those members, and repeating the process until no new members of the population are identified.[4]

A census of hammer mills in operation at the time of the study identified 122 hammer mills in the four cities. To locate the hammer mills, a previous census of hammer mills done by the Department of Agricultural Economics and Extension at the University of Zimbabwe was used as a basis for the search[5]. All the hammer mills on that list were visited and surveyed. At the same time, both the operators and customers of each hammer mill visited were asked if they knew of any other hammer mills in that neighbourhood.

Using this snowball sampling technique, about 50 other hammer mills were identified, visited and surveyed. Research team members, who lived in many different parts of Harare and Chitungwiza, also used their knowledge of their own communities to identify a number of mills in their own neighbourhoods. The same snowball sampling technique then proceeded from each of those mills until no new mills could be identified.

Of the 122 mills identified by the survey, 86 were available for interviewing. The operators of these 86 mills were then interviewed to examine both the response of hammer millers to the recent reforms and the millers' role in the new market environment.

In addition, at the hammer mills, a total of 1,528 people were randomly selected from the queues and interviewed to examine the impact of the removal of the subsidy on consumption patterns and accessibility of maize meal within their households. These interviews with hammer mill consumers were conducted on all seven days of the week and at different times during the day, in order to ensure a representative sample of hammer mill customers. It cannot be claimed that the people interviewed were representative of maize consumers, since this was obviously a particular sub-set of the maize market consumers. However, a representative sample of all maize consumers was not needed to fulfil the terms of reference of the study, only a representative sample of hammer mill customers (Table 5.1).

Table 5.1
Distribution of respondents by city

City	Number
Harare	611
Bulawayo	437
Mutare	197
Chitungwiza	283
Total	1,528

Two major manufacturers of hammer mills in Zimbabwe were also contacted to obtain information on their sales of hammer mills. Both previous and on-going studies related to the urban Zimbabwean maize market were also reviewed to double check the findings of this research.

The methodology outlined above, as well as the questionnaires[6] used in the survey, were discussed extensively within the Ministry of Public Service, Labour and Social Welfare and UNICEF. Outside experts in the University of Zimbabwe, the Ministry of Lands, Agriculture and Water Development, and the Grain Marketing Board also provided valuable inputs into the discussions of methodology and research instrument design.

2.2 Limitations of the study

The data were obtained from millers and their customers through formal interviews with a pre-coded questionnaire. Thus the results suffer from the usual limitations of questionnaire-based research.

Although the research team was quite confident that all of the hammer millers in the three urban areas were discovered, an inherent limitation of the sampling method was that one can never be certain that one has

69

identified the whole universe of cases. It was possible that some hammer mills went unnoticed in the survey, especially in the low density neighbourhoods. If this was the case, then this survey was underestimating the production capacity of the hammer milling sector and underestimating the access of urban consumers to mugayiwa.

Since time and budget limitations made it impossible to interview a representative sample of maize consumers but only a sample of hammer mill customers, the estimates of price elasticity of demand could not be generalised to all consumers. These estimates could, however, be considered a good indicator of the willingness of low income urban maize consumers to buy yellow maize at various rates of discount, since the hammer mill customers could be assumed to be low income earners.

Finally, seasonality is an important question in any survey related to the economics of food. This report took measurements at only a single point during the year, i.e. in October-November and thus could not take seasonality fully into account. This was compensated for by considering the results of another, similar study conducted in July, 1993.

3. Prices of mugayiwa and roller meal in October-November 1993

Before the June 1993 price liberalisation, the subsidised price of a 5 kg bag of roller meal was Z$5.82. After the subsidy was removed, the price rose by roughly 50 percent, to Z$8.83 in most urban stores. The price of larger bags of roller meal were almost exactly in proportion to the size of the bag, both before and after the price liberalisation; that is, a 10 kg bag was almost exactly twice the price of a 5 kg bag. In other words, there were no significant economies of scale or bulk discounts in buying larger bags of roller meal. For simplicity sake, therefore, the rest of the analysis concentrated on the 5 kg bag of meal. Virtually the same results would have been obtained by using the 10 kg, 20 kg or 50 kg bag in the analysis. The fundamental results and implications are the same regardless of the size of bag.

The survey found that straight run maize (mugayiwa) was available in urban areas in October-November 1993 for an average of Z$5.50 per 5 kg. Using the dispersion of prices, weight of maize per bucket and milling costs, high- and low-cost scenarios for the price of mugayiwa were also created, showing that 5 kg of mugayiwa costs between Z$4.70 and Z$7.25.

These estimates were calculated in the following manner. Half of hammer mill customers (51 percent) reported that they bought whole grain maize in town and then took it to the mill for milling into maize meal. Most of the rest of the hammer mill customers (31 percent) said they brought their own maize in from rural areas and had it milled in town, presumably because this was cheaper than buying it in town.[10] However, the urban buying price of maize was used as a proxy for the cost of maize to the household in this survey, even though it may overestimate the cost to many households.

The standard measure of whole grain maize in urban areas in Zimbabwe is the bucket. A bucket is a metal container of standard size used throughout markets in Zimbabwe. A bucket contains 16-18 kg of whole grain maize when full; the weight of the maize depends on its moisture content. Shortly after harvest time, the moisture content will likely be greater than later on. The interviews with the 910 hammer mill customers who said they bought their maize grain indicate that they paid between Z$7.00 and Z$25.00 for a bucket of maize, with a mean price of Z$16.58. The dispersion of prices was quite small: 80 percent of the interviewees reported paying between Z$14 and Z$18 per bucket. Only 2 percent of respondents said they could not remember how much they paid for a bucket of maize grain. The price figures reported by respondents were confirmed as realistic and representative by the research team, who also checked the prices of whole grain maize in urban markets.

The range of milling fees charged by the hammer millers per bucket was from Z$0.80 to Z$3.50. The most common (modal) fee was Z$2.00 per bucket, charged by 35 of the 86 millers. The average (mean) milling fee was Z$1.70. Most of the millers had a sign outside indicating the cost of milling a bucket of maize.

The average rate of wastage in a hammer mill is 2 percent.[8] This was also factored into all the calculations. At an average price of Z$16.58 per bucket of maize, and assuming 17 kg of maize per bucket and a milling wastage rate of 2 percent, the average price per kg of whole grain maize was Z$1.00. Adding in Z$1.70 for the cost of milling a bucket, the price per 5 kg of mugayiwa was found to be Z$5.50.

The high and low estimates of Z$4.70 and Z$7.05 per 5 kg mentioned above were arrived at by creating high-cost and low-cost scenarios out of the above data ranges.

For example, the high-cost scenario of Z$7.05 for 5 kg assumed the following:

a) only 16 kg of maize to a bucket
b) a higher than average price of maize grain (Z$20.00 per bucket; less than 1 percent of consumers reported paying more than Z$20 per bucket),
c) the modal milling fee of Z$2.00 per bucket, and
d) the standard wastage rate of 2 percent.

71

The low-cost scenario of Z$4.70 for 5 kg assumed the following:
a)   18 kg of maize grain per bucket
b)   a lower than average price of maize grain (Z$15 per bucket; 90 percent of consumers paid Z$15/bucket or more)
c)   the average milling fee of Z$1.70 per bucket, and
d)   the standard wastage rate of 2 percent.

Even in the highest cost scenario, mugayiwa was still cheaper than roller meal by 20 percent (Z$8.83 vs. Z$7.05 for 5 kg). The price of mugayiwa in the middle range scenario (Z$5.50 per 5 kg) was 38 percent lower than the price of roller meal, and the price of mugayiwa in the lowest cost scenario was 47 percent lower than the price of roller meal. In other words, straight run maize meal was available at prices considerably cheaper than roller meal.

4. The real price of roller meal

But was mugayiwa cheaper than the old subsidised price of roller meal, before June 1993? Let us compare the prices of roller meal at various times in the recent past, and deflate them to October 1993 prices, using the official Central Statistical Office (CSO) consumer price index (CSO, 1994).

Table 5.2
Nominal and real prices of 5 kg bag of roller meal, various dates

Date	Price per kg bag	CSO Price Index (1990 = 100)	Real October 1993 Price
Oct. 1993	8.83	238.0	8.83
May 1993	5.82	215.0	6.46
Aug. 1992	5.82	185.3	7.45
July 1992	3.88	176.9	5.24
Feb. 1992	3.88	146.5	6.29
Jan. 1992	3.23	142.7	5.39
June 1991	3.23	123.3	6.23
June 1990	2.17	100.0	5.16

Source: *Ziana, The Herald, Department of Information (Maize Prices), CSO (Price Index)*

As the above table shows, the real price of roller meal has varied, due to the inflation in the long periods between price changes. Price changes were announced in May 1991, February and August 1992 and June 1993. However, the price of roller meal expressed in constant October 1993 dollars has consistently been comparable to or higher than the current average price of mugayiwa (i.e. Z$5.50 per 5 kg). The high-cost scenario for the October 1993 price of mugayiwa (Z$7.05 per 5 kg) was well within the range of real price fluctuations of roller meal in the last two years. The current (1993) average price of mugayiwa (Z$5.50 per 5 kg) was only 7 percent higher than the real pre-ESAP price of roller meal of Z$5.16 per 5 kg. The current low-cost scenario for the price of mugayiwa was well below the real price of roller meal throughout the period since June 1990.

Cheap staple food was available to the poor urban consumer at prices lower than or comparable to pre-ESAP subsidised maize prices, without any drain on the public treasury. Under ESAP, urban consumers may save on food costs by switching from roller meal to mugaiwa. The savings on costs could be high if residents grow their own maize and not buy from the market.

4. Availability, production and consumption of maize meal

Straight run maize meal was available in large quantities in urban areas. The mean production capacity reported by the 86 mills surveyed was 82 tonnes per month, assuming the mills operate 10 hours per day Monday to Friday and 8.5 hours per day on weekends, with two days of breakdown and repair time per month. This was very similar to the results of an earlier study done by MLAWD and USAID, which estimated the average monthly production capacity of hammer mills in urban Zimbabwe to be 90 tonnes per month. It was also consistent with what was known about the production capacity of hammer mills sold in Zimbabwe. Extrapolating this production capacity to all 122 mills, means that the monthly production capacity of all the identified mills was 9,992 tonnes per month.

Consumption of maize meal was estimated for the purposes of this study to be 17,558 tonnes of maize per month in the urban areas surveyed. This estimate was based on the following calculations. At the August 1992 census, there were 543,099 urban households in Bulawayo, Mutare and Harare Province (including Epworth and Chitungwiza). Assuming a 6 percent growth rate in urban areas over the 14 months since the census (CSO, 1993), this gave a total of 575,685 households in mid-October 1993, the start of the study. Average urban consumption of maize meal according to Ministry of Lands, Agriculture and Water

Development was 30.5 kg per household per month (MLAWD/USAID, 1993).

Combining the production monthly capacity of the 122 hammer mills (9,992 tonnes) with the consumption of maize meal (17,558 tonnes), the hammer millers' production capacity was equivalent to 57 percent of the demand for maize meal in urban areas. Assuming that only the 86 mills which were actually interviewed were in operation, the production capacity of the millers was equivalent to 40 percent of urban consumption. Probably the real proportion of the urban market satisfied by the hammer millers was somewhere in between these two figures. Thus, and even allowing for the fact that some of this straight run maize would move back to the rural areas and some used for making animal feed, the hammer millers could satisfy an important part of the urban demand for maize meal. Some 93 percent of the millers (N=80/86) reported that they milled for human consumption, only 7 percent mills for animal feed.

Another study, conducted in July 1993 by the Ministry of Lands, Agriculture and Water Development with support from USAID, found similar results. Using a slightly different methodology, that study found that hammer mill production was equivalent to 66 percent of urban consumption; 27 percent of urban households said they consumed straight run maize meal (MLAWD/USAID, 1993). In interpreting these results, it should be remembered that the number of hammer mills in operation at the time of the MLAWD/USAID study (July 1993) was much smaller than the number at 1993. It could thus be expected that the proportion of households consuming mugayiwa had increased from the 27 percent found in the MLAWD/USAID survey.

5. Distribution of Hammer Mills and changes in the maize market

The survey found 85 hammer millers in Harare and Chitungwiza, 27 in Bulawayo, and 10 in Mutare. Most of the 122 hammer mills were located in high density suburbs (57 percent, N=70) where the majority of poor urban consumers live, or in industrial areas (11 percent, N=13) where many of the same population work. All the major high density suburbs in Harare, Chitungwiza, Bulawayo and Mutare have at least one hammer mill.

Number of hammer mills

The operators of hammer mills were asked when they first started operations. Using these answers, it was possible to track the growth of the hammer mill industry over the last few years. The results show that there has been a small revolution in the maize market since the June 1993 reforms (see Figure 5.1). The number of hammer millers increased from 71 to 122 between June and November 1993. As the number of hammer mills increased, so too did the availability of cheap maize meal to urban consumers.

Table 5.3
Number of Hammer Mills, various dates

Date	Number of mills
November 1993	122
June 1993	71
January 1993	58
January 1992	55
January 1991	47
January 1990	45

The growth in the number of hammer mills in use in urban areas was consistent with a pattern of sales growth reported by two major hammer mill manufacturers in Zimbabwe. Sales in 1992 were 27 percent higher than in 1990; sales in the first seven months of 1993 equalled sales for the whole of 1992 (see Figure 5.2)

Consumption trends of mugayiwa and roller meal

Of the 1,528 consumers of straight run meal interviewed for this survey in October and November. 1993, fully 21 percent started consuming it in June 1993, immediately after the price hike for roller meal. Fifty four percent said they started consuming mugayiwa between June and October 1993. Ninety one percent said they started consuming mugayiwa since January 1993. Eighty four percent of the mugayiwa consumers interviewed said that they ate mugayiwa for every sadza meal in the household.

This tremendous increase in mugayiwa consumption in urban areas was documented in other surveys as well. In 1992, only 5-8 percent of urban maize consumption was in the form of mugayiwa; yet the MLAWD/USAID survey found 27 percent of 512 households in Harare, Chitungwiza and Bulawayo consumed mugayiwa as their main staple in July 1993 (MLAWD/USAID, 1993). Preliminary findings from the fourth round of sentinel surveillance conducted by the Inter-Ministerial Committee for SDA Monitoring found that 48 percent of the 1,575 urban households interviewed ate mugayiwa in May 1993, but 76 percent ate

Figure 5.1
Growth in number of hammer mills in operation in Harare, Chitungwiza, Bulawayo

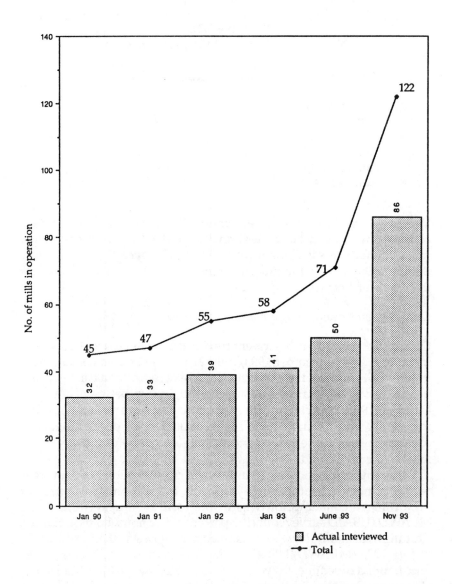

Figure 5.2
Total sales of Hammer Mills by two leading manufacturers
Jan 1988 – 31st July 1993

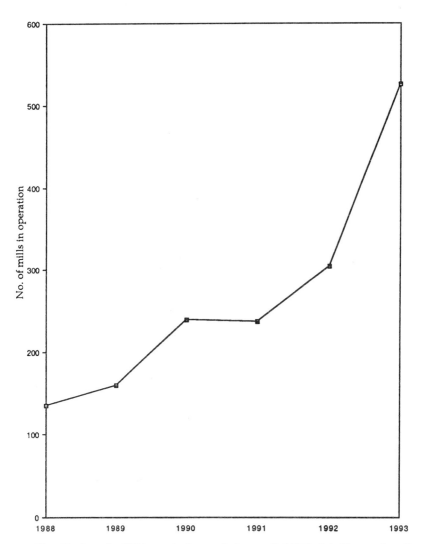

Note: The figure for 1993 is a projection,; total sales equalled 306 by July 31st, ceteris paribus

mugayiwa in November 1993 (Inter-Ministerial Committee, forthcoming).

This increase in mugayiwa consumption coincides with the price changes for roller meal. Asked why they consume straight run, 62 percent of the mugayiwa consumers interviewed in this survey said they switched because of the price increase for roller meal in June 1993; a further 17 percent said they switched because of the roller meal price increase in August 1992; another 7 percent said they ate mugayiwa because it had always been cheaper than roller meal. In all, 91 percent of mugayiwa consumers in this survey said that their choice was driven by the price of mugayiwa relative to the price of roller meal; mugayiwa was simply cheaper.

The results of this survey confirm the findings of the earlier MLAWD/ USAID survey that urban maize meal choice was overwhelmingly driven by price considerations. In the earlier survey, 80 percent of mugayiwa consumers had switched from roller meal due to the price difference (MLAWD/USAID, 1993). Earlier surveys have documented the declining consumption of super refined meal as its price rose (Inter-Ministerial Committee, 1993a); this was further evidence of the price-sensitivity of maize meal consumption choices in urban Zimbabwe.

Accessibility of mugayiwa to urban consumers

The switch to mugayiwa was facilitated not only by the relative prices of mugayiwa and roller meal, but also by accessibility. As noted above, the number of hammer mills in operation appears to be growing quickly, and sales by hammer mill makers are up dramatically in 1993. Also, the presence of hammer mills in all the major high density neighbourhoods of Harare, Chitungwiza, Bulawayo and Mutare seems to encourage access even by low income groups. Mugayiwa consumption appears to be concentrated in the lower-income portions of urban society (MLAWD/USAID, 1993).

But what of accessibility in terms of time spent to get the mugayiwa? The 1,528 mugayiwa consumers exiting from the hammer mill were asked how much time they spent in getting to the hammer mill and in waiting in the queue. The average time spent walking to the hammer mill (one way) was 22 minutes; 86 percent spent 30 minutes or less walking to the hammer mill. In addition, the waiting time in the queue averaged 43 minutes; 77 percent of mugayiwa mill customers reported waiting for between 5 and 60 minutes in the queue.

Mugayiwa consumers were also asked how much time it took them to go to the store the last time that they bought roller meal. The average time taken in going to the store was 11 minutes, half of the time typically spent walking to a hammer mill. Presumably the time spent waiting in the queue at a store or supermarket was also less than the 43 minutes spent on average in a hammer mill queue.

Increasing numbers of urban consumers, however, obviously consider the extra time spent getting mugayiwa to be worthwhile. Of the 1,528 mugayiwa consumers interviewed in this survey, only 6 percent suggested that waiting in a queue was a problem that their household faced in getting maize meal[9]. This suggests that the opportunity cost of time spent in queues was thought to be low. Given the very high unemployment rates in high density neighbourhoods (thought to be 30 percent or more), many low income households are likely to have one or more members who have sufficient time to spend in a hammer mill queue.

Yellow maize vs white maize grain and seasonality

Respondents in the hammer mill queues were asked at what price (if any) they would start buying whole grain yellow maize if it were available at lower prices than white maize grain[10]. (The average price of white maize grain in urban markets was Z$16.58 per bucket.)

The results show a considerable willingness to purchase yellow maize, if the price were right (see Table 5.4 and Figure 5.3). Again, these results are not meant to be representative of the population of maize consumers as a whole, but can probably give a good indication of the willingness of low-income consumers to buy yellow maize grain at subsidised prices.

Table 5.4
Willingness of current mugayiwa consumers to buy yellow maize grain at discount

Proposed price/bucket	No. willing to buy yellow maize grain	% willing to buy yellow maize grain
Z$15.00	359	23%
Z$13.50	537	35%
Z$12.75	592	39%
Z$12.00	690	45%
Z$11.25	739	48%
Z$10.50	922	60%
Z$9.00	1,010	66%
Under Z$9.00	1,064	70%

N = 1,528

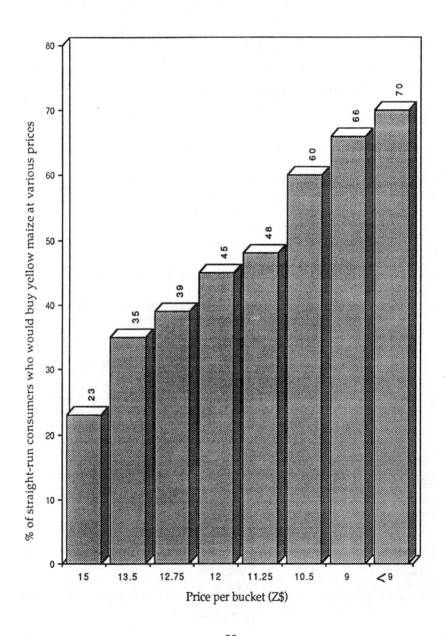

Figure 5.3
At what price would you buy yellow maize
in preference to white maize?

These results indicate that subsidising yellow whole grain maize could be an effective way of supplementing urban food security of low income households while helping GMB dispose of excess yellow maize stocks.

The ability of urban households to save part of their incomes spent on maize meal by procuring it via the hammer mill and the magnitude of these savings would certainly depend on the availability and reliability of maize grain supplies in the cities. Availability of maize supplies and hence demand for hammer milling services has traditionally been seasonal, peaking during the harvest period (July to September) and dropping to minimum levels in the pre-harvest months (December, January and February). This survey took place at an intermediate season (October-November).

In 1993, the demand for milling service in October was lower than that in May among 46 millers interviewed; was higher among 10 and had not changed among 6. Moreover,of the 703 mugayiwa consumers who reported growing their own maize either in rural or urban areas, 45 percent (N=313/703) said they would deplete their maize stocks before the next harvest and would have to resort to purchases of maize grain or maize meal. Maize grain prices also tend to follow the same pattern, being higher in months of scarcity. The availability of subsidised yellow maize meal could, therefore, help bridge this supply gap and keep maize prices affordable to the urban poor, especially just before harvest.

6. Conclusions

The hammer milling industry is capable of supplying over half of the urban population (and an even greater proportion of the urban poor) with low-cost maize meal. Furthermore, the number of hammer mills is growing rapidly and the industry will soon be able to satisfy even greater demand. Consumption data indicate that at least a quarter of the urban population consume straight run maize meal from hammer mills and that their choice was overwhelmingly driven by price considerations. Many consumers of mugayiwa also showed a willingness to purchase yellow maize grain for hammer milling if the price was lower than the price of white maize grain.

One implication of the findings of this survey was that urban nutrition may improve due to the switch to mugayiwa, which was more nutritious than roller meal. Mugayiwa contains 8-20 percent more protein, 17-150 percent more thiamin, 62-100 percent more riboflavin, 25-127 percent more iron, and 71-100 percent more calcium than the moderately- and super-refined products from a roller mill.[11]

The extraction rate for hammer mills was much higher (about 98 percent) than for industrial roller mills (about 85 percent); in other words, a given quantity of maize will yield more meal if milled in a hammer mill. National food security may be enhanced by the shift to hammer milling from roller milling.

Hammer milling technology is more labour-intensive, less skill-intensive, and demands a smaller initial capital outlay than roller milling technology. The expansion of the hammer milling industry may thus promote employment creation and the development of small and medium-scale enterprises.

One major implication for the Ministry of Public Service, Labour and Social Welfare of the shift to mugayiwa concerns the Food Money Scheme under the Social Development Fund. The Food Money Scheme was premised on compensating poor urban households for the financial hardship imposed on them by the removal of the roller meal subsidy. But if mugayiwa was available in large quantities at prices comparable to or lower than the old subsidised price of roller meal, then this justification is vitiated. The resources and staff devoted to the Food Money Scheme could be better employed elsewhere.

However, if it was judged that even the widespread availability of mugayiwa at relatively low real prices was not sufficient to cushion the urban poor, then the subsidising of yellow maize could prove to be a more cost-effective way to help than the current Food Money Scheme. Since the Food Money Scheme relies on individual households applying for assistance, it was very intensive in its use of administrative resources[12]. Targeting of yellow maize sales rather than targeting of individual households might be a more efficient use of scarce administrative resources.

ESAP has resulted in the decrease in real wages of the poor urban residents while prices for the food commodities to be purchased have increased. Urban households spend over 15 percent of their incomes on food purchases. Such a situation demands that households be innovative. This chapter has shown how urban families adjust from one commodity (roller meal) to another (mugaiwa), a feature which has led to an increase in the hammer mill industry.

Growing of own food in the backyard or on public open spaces becomes a reasonable alternative under these circumstances. In this situation, sources of maize grain for urban residents are expanded. They now include inflows from rural areas, inflows from commercial farms and small holdings in the peri-urban areas, purchases from major grain marketing institutions such as the Grain Marketing Board and outputs from urban cultivation. There is need (as part of ongoing studies) to proceed and capture the proportion of urban maize grain contributed by each of these sources throughout the year.

Notes

1. Modified from a research report by The Ministry of Public Service, Labour and Social Welfare, Zimbabwe (funded by UNICEF, Harare, March 1994)
2. At March 1994, Munhamo Chisvo was consultant and Visiting Lecturer in Department of Economics, University of Zimbabwe. Mrs W.O. Goromonzi was Assistant Research and Statistics Officer in the Ministry of Public Service, Labour and Social Welfare, Harare. Mr Lauchlan Munro was Program Officer, UNICEF-Harare.
3. Maize meal or mealie-meal is the flour from maize/corn used to prepare "sadza"; a thick porridge which is the stable food for black Zimbabweans.
4. Johnson and Joslyn (1986), Political Science Research Methods, Congressional Quarterly Press, Washington DC
5. Rubey L and Jayne T.S. Maize milling, Market Reform and Urban Food Security; The Case of Zimbabwe. Working Paper AEE 4/92, Department of Agricultural Economics, UZ, Harare
6. Copy of questionnaire can be made available on request
7. The proportions buying bringing in whole grain maize from the rural areas will vary greatly by season. This survey was conducted mid-way between the harvests, which occur roughly in March-April in communal areas.
8. Bagachwa M.S.D. (1991) Choice of Technology in Industry: The Economics of Grain Milling in Tanzania, IDRC, Ottawa
9. Almost 19%, however, said that transport or distance posed significant problems to their households in obtaining maize meal. Fifty five percent said that their household faced "no problem" in acquiring maize meal.
10. White maize meal is preferred to yellow maize meal. The latter has been consumed during drought years when it is made available as drought relief. Normally it is reserved for stock feed.
11. West C. et.al (1987) Food Composition Table. Mimeo, Wageningen Agricultural University, The Netherlands
12. Details are available from Kaseke E. (1993) A Situation Analysis of the Social Development Fund, Ministry of The Public Service , Labour and Social Welfare and Unicef, Harare and ILO (1993) Structural Adjustment in Zimbabwe, Occasional Paper No. 16, Geneva.

6 Institutional Responses to Uncontrolled Urban Cultivation in Harare: Prohibitive or Accommodative?

1, Introduction

This chapter reviews institutional responses to uncontrolled urban cultivation[1] in Harare with a view to establish whether such responses are accommodative or prohibitive and what the future approaches could be. The only time when urban cultivation becomes an issue of general concern in Zimbabwe is when urban local authorities invoke their development control powers to destroy/slash crops alleged to be illegally grown on urban council land. In Harare (the capital city), the manner in which this slashing has been done and subsequently reported in the press, portrays a picture of an insensitive and prohibitive local authority. It paints a view of a local authority which only acts at the last minute; one which does not engage in long term planning on the issue of urban cultivation.

In the second part the chapter provides a working outline of what constitutes an accommodative or a prohibitive local authority. This provides a framework to start a review of institutional responses to urban cultivation in Harare. Using a historical approach part 3 traces these institutional responses in a detailed descriptive and informative manner. Part 4 reviews the sustainability and effectiveness of the

85

responses to urban cultivation providing comments as to why local authorities find it difficult to sustainably and effectively manage urban cultivation.

Local authorities have to respond to the phenomenon basically because of the perceived environmental problems it may create plus the real land use conflicts it has generated. But because of the economic, environmental and gender dimensions that are related to it, misplaced local authority responses can do more harm than good. On the other hand, can we afford urban agriculture in view of demands for urban land considering an urbanisation rate of 4.5 percent per year in Harare (or a housing waiting list of close to one hundred thousand families.

The conclusion notes that under continued unfavourable economic conditions in Zimbabwe compounded by pressures due to rapid urban population growth, urban residents have to find alternative informal means of survival. Uncontrolled urban cultivation is likely to be on the increase even in the face of prohibitive measures thus leaving accommodative approaches as the only option for managing this phenomenon.

2. Structural overview of the local authority

For those not familiar with the local authority in Zimbabwe in general and Harare City Council in particular, it may be necessary to provide a brief sketch of the local authority's major components. Although local, the local authority is partly a central government creation and tied to it through Ministry of Local Government Rural and Urban Development. Through this 'parent' Ministry, central government imposes controls, monitors and interferes with operations of local government on matters of urban land, housing, finance, appointment and election of office bearers e.t.c. The degree of interference is determined statutorily by the Urban Councils' Act, The Regional Town and Country Planning Act and other unwritten codes depending on personalities and political climate in the country.

The local authority itself is made up of the elected wing (councillors) on one hand and the appointed professionals on the other. Councillors are elected by communities every two years to serve on council. There is a councillor for each of the 24 wards. Once elected, the councillors elect a mayor from among themselves. They also elect councillors to be heads of committees[2] of council whose membership will include professionals.

Then there are the non-elected agencies of council in the form of service provision oriented departments[3] usually headed by a director who will be an expert in the given service sector. These heads of departments or their appointees sit on council committees providing council with technical advice. They also manage the day to day issues relating to the provision of their services.

The Town Clerk heads the Town Clerk's Department as a professional. But at the same time, he/she is chief executive or chief spokesman of the council. The Town Clerk is also secretariat to the council and can be viewed as a linchpin in the system. This elevates him above other heads of departments.

A wide range of pressure groups also exist. They include the political parties and groups of experts, non-governmental organisations e.t.c. As it turns out to be, all the above categories (as institutions and the individuals who hold offices in them) relate directly or indirectly to the communities. Local government in some respects is a struggle to sustain control of these relations with the communities.

3 The accommodative and the prohibitive local authority

The institution charged with the management of a local spatial unit be it a city or rural district is generally labelled as 'a local authority'. The actual title given varies from country to country. For urban areas, the variation also takes into account the size of the area. Development planning literature is awash with debates on the economics, the politics and the management of local areas. The financing of local government activities and centre-local relations (i.e. how the local authorities relate to the state authority) are some of the themes where debate is still ongoing. Community participation in local authority affairs is also another area of debate with recent interest on local authority accountability.

It is not the intention to debate details of these issues here, but to simply acknowledge the their existence and warn that the concept of 'accommodative and prohibitive' may be similar to some concepts already in use elsewhere or that those seasoned in local government debates may find them a bit elementary. They should however suffice for the objective of assessing the level of strategic planning and relations to the community which prevail in Harare vis a vis the phenomenon of urban agriculture.

An accommodative local authority will be taken as one that engages in strategic planning for issues critical to the survival of its populace. It is an evaluative, enabling, democratic and pluralistic authority. Enabling implies ability and willingness to provide or encourage a diversity of alternative views and ways of managing the local area in response to people's needs. Reception to new ideas, adapting laws/regulations to changing conditions and interacting with the communities are key attributes of such an authority. This does not rule out disagreement with these communities but that confrontation as a way for resolving these disagreements is minimised. Here the community is the master and the authority the facilitator.

On the other hand, the prohibitive local authority is strategically rigid; using blue prints which are hardly adapted to changing circumstances. This is a very centralised authority, distanced from communities and not taking easily to new ideas. It makes laws and rigidly operates in conformity with these laws. Therefore lack of flexibility and an aloofness from communities is a key attribute. Here the authority is the master, all omnipresent and omnipotent.

In these definitions there has been no attempt to separate the executive arm of local authority (such as the technical departments) from the political arms (such as the mayor of the city and councillors). How these interact among themselves and also how they relate to the outside world are issues with a significant bearing on a discussion of urban cultivation in Harare.

4. The Harare experience: institutional responses

The colonial era (1980 inheritance)

Colonial urban development viewed the urban African as a sojourner in the city. No long term plans for his/her accommodation were made. His/her presence was supposed to provide cheap labour in the factories and homes of the then colonial settlers. To supplement the meagre and often sporadic income, the urban African had to grow crops around the workplace and the temporary urban home. Most of this was to supplement domestic food requirements while in the urban area. There were two basic responses to this by the then urban administrators.

First they used access to urban cultivation as an excuse to pay the Urban African low wages. Secondly, foreseeing the environmental damage likely from the activity[4], conservation programmes were initiated. These included demarcation and pegging of areas to be cultivated or not to be cultivated. Such pegging was still visible at independence in 1980 in areas such as Mabvuku and Tafara. A number of regulations were passed to assist in the conservation campaigns. These included:

(a) Salisbury Protection of Lands By Laws, 1973, Rhodesia Govt. Notice No. 104 of 1973

(b) Salisbury Protection of Lands By Laws, 1975 Rhodesia Govt. Notice No. 840 of 1975 (No.1)
(c) Salisbury Protection of Lands By laws, 1975, Statutory Instrument 545 of 1979.
(d) Natural Resources (Protection) Regulations 1979

These regulations were developed by the Dept. of Natural Resources[5] and not the local authorities; an item for the centre-local relations debate. The local authorities were to use these as frameworks for their own by-laws.

Thus for exploitative reasons, urban cultivation was accommodated in the pre-1980 era while recognition of its potential damage to the environment led to conservation measures buttressed by legal regulations. This is what was inherited at 1980.

The reconnaissance phase (early 1980 s)

At independence in 1980 the Department of Natural Resources and local authorities inherited cities with urban cultivation managed with a supporting string of conservation regulations. The Harare Municipality had no plans nor policy to manage urban cultivation. All its actions were prompted by requests and comments of other actors especially Department of Natural Resources and the Natural Resources Board. Referring to urban cultivation the Director of Housing and Community Services in a memo to Director of Works wrote thus:

> "The Natural Resources Board would like this matter raised in council and a proper policy formulated in this regard in so far as the city is concerned.[6]

Therefore unless probed by some external agent or institutions, the city council was content to let the existing situation prevail; turning a blind eye to the activity. The Department of Natural Resources initiated further discussions with the Mayor of Harare. In February 1982, the Department invited the Mayor and some councillors for a flight over the city to give them an aerial view of the damage to natural resources within and around the city as a result of cultivation and tree felling. Complementing the flight invitation, the Department of Natural Resources also indicated its readiness to co-operate with the council in designing a conservation policy. It went further to offer material and manpower resources for monitoring conservation programmes and education campaigns. Concluding this offer, the Department indicated that:

"It is also hoped that the councillors being leaders of the people in their areas would always bring the subject at community meetings, clubs and rallies. Action needs to be started now in order to avoid embarrassment by stopping cultivation when people have already started planting crops" [7]

The flight, subsequently took place on 11 th April 1982. This was followed by further discussions and correspondences with another flight in June 1982. Following this flight, the Mayor of Harare (then Dr Gwata) commented that;

"Suburbs are like deserts. It is really startling if you compare some areas with others. There should be positive encouragement for tree planting at all levels with assistance from council, the Natural Resources Board and other organisations. [8]

The Mayor also called for stricter enforcement of laws against uncontrolled cultivation especially along river banks. In general, a number of strategies were attempted in the early 1980s, and a number of institutions contributed to these efforts in varying degrees. These were the Department of Natural Resources, Harare City Council, Harare West — Intensive Conservation Authority and the Natural Resources Board.

Information campaign

This included issuing of notices to the public to help them understand the laws governing urban cultivation and illegal destruction of natural resources around the city. The notices in Shona[9] and English were distributed to all households and some placed in valleys 30 metres away from streams affected. The notices warned against illegal cultivation quoting the Natural Resources (Protection) Regulations 1975, indicated that no person was allowed to cultivate within 30 (thirty) metres of the naturally defined banks of a Public stream. Crops illegally grown would be slashed and fines of up to Z$1 000,00 (one thousand Zimbabwe dollars) imposed on offenders.

The law was meant to protect streams from potential siltation resulting from soil erosion on the cultivated areas. Citing the Save River,[10] the publications and notices warned that siltation of rivers was a threat to water supplies to the city. Although slashing threats were given, no slashing was done till 1986. It is not clear whether any resident was penalised for cultivation either.

Education, dermacation and pegging campaign

In addition to notices and publications, more meetings and discussions were held to educate councillors and council officials. Radio programmes and education programmes were also introduced in schools with the Ministry of Education involvement. Efforts were also made to involve school pupils in tree planting sessions. At the same time, the city council was involved in dermacation and pegging of areas suitable for cultivation. This was done to assist in monitoring stream bank cultivation. Although allocation of land was not a policy, this demarcation would implicitly guide households on where to cultivate and where not to cultivate. The cost of this exercise was made high because residents destroyed or vandalised the pegs. Secondly, it is an exercise to be done annually to take care of new land use proposals and development.

Use of municipal security unit

From these early days, it was realised that technical officers monitoring urban cultivation were at risk from attacks by cultivators and that the destruction of notices was an offence act requiring police action. Subsequently, as early as August 1982, the local authority had allocated 32 police officers to monitor urban cultivation activities in the high density areas. Each patrolman would be remunerated at approximately Z$12.61 for an eight hour shift, plus mileage and supervision.[11] The cost of this service was made higher because the areas to be patrolled were too broad. Cultivating residents further resorted to cultivating early in the morning or late in the evening (effectively increasing daylight hours) thus stretching the police's working hours and thereby increasing council's monitoring costs.

Greater Harare illegal cultivation committee

Attempts were also made to complement existing units by setting up strategy forming committees. In the Department of Housing and Community Services, the Health Housing and Community Services Committee researched and provided most of the options eventually adopted by council. A pressure group, Greater Harare Illegal Cultivation Committee was also set up in 1983, dissolved in 1986 and revived in December 1989 after representations from Department of Natural Resources.[12] The committee would look into the problems of environmental degradation in Harare and recommend appropriate action and co-ordinate institutional deliberations on the issue. It was made up of representatives from:

1. Representatives from H/Q Department of Natural Resources
2. Officers from Regions, North, West, East and South Intensive Conservation Area Committees

3. Municipal Security Unit — Harare City Town Clerk's Department

4. Director of Works Representative — Harare City

5. Ministry of Education

6. Zimbabwe Republic Police

7. Agritex (Ministry of Agriculture and Water Development)

8. ZANU (PF) Harare (Main Wing, Women and Young Wings)

9. Department of Housing and Community Services

Politicians: contributions in the early years

The participation of the politicians in the early 1980s is worth reviewing. First is the participation of the ZANU (PF) 'wings' on the Greater Harare Illegal cultivation Committee. ZANU (PF) — the ruling party since 1980- represents(ed) the majority's wishes and such participation meant that urban cultivation strategies would be known to the ruling party leadership before implementation thus minimising political conflicts.

The ruling party at that time sympathised with local authority positions on urban cultivation. This is not surprising given that the majority of councillors in office were also ZANU (PF) members. Worth noting in this regard is a comment in 1982, by the then Minister of Mines, Mr Maurice Nyagumbo who was also ZANU (PF)'s National Organising Secretary. He urged city Councillors to stop people growing crops on stream banks and the destruction of natural resources in urban areas as this was becoming a threat to the main water supplies.. The Minister told a party's Mashonaland East Province political seminar in Harare that Zimbabwe's cities and towns had to be tough against stream bank cultivators because cultivators were threatening sources of water.

> "If people want to go into full scale farming, they must apply to Government for proper resettlement. They produce nothing but cause a lot of siltation of our sources of water. They must go before they do more harm than good. Zimbabweans must know that urban areas and farming areas are different. They must not do as they please. They must follow the regulations and adhere to them. City Councils must act now and stop this"[13]

The Minister further criticized councillors who sympathised with "irresponsible and undisciplined residents" for fear of losing popularity in their wards. ZANU (PF) was determined to stop this practice and any councillor who did not act against it (urban cultivation) would be flushed out by the party because he/she would have gone out of step.

Thus a political framework and terms of reference on the issue were set. Consequently, in these early years, all councillors made an effort to dissociate themselves from urban cultivators through direct participation in Council's strategies or refuting any allegations of sympathy towards cultivators.

The Repressive confrontational phase; 1985 and beyond

The period between 1980 and 1985 was one where institutions tried to forge a common understanding on urban cultivation. Gradually through efforts and continued pressure from environmentalists, the City of Harare was forced to come up with some loose policy responses to urban cultivation. Political and technical support was also forthcoming though it is not clear how much financial support was made available. However by 1984 it was obvious that all attempts to halt cultivation had been in vain.

In 1985, Council still used pre-1980 by-laws despite calls to amend these with respect to urban cultivation. Officers on the ground were getting disillusioned by lack of a corporate approach by their seniors in the local authority. Allocation of responsibility between the Department of Works, Town Clerk and DHCS were in most cases not clear. Further, any activities these Departments initiated would not find ready funding from the City Treasurer. The cost of current strategies was considered wasteful given that cultivation continued and vandalism of notices and trees planted could not be controlled.

In November 1985, site visits by the Mayor and professionals from NRB, Department of Works, DCHS found all pegs previously put down to demarcate areas in Marimba and Sunningdale areas destroyed. At that stage the whole urban cultivation management activity was quoted as costing council Z$250,00 (two hundred and fifty Zimbabwe dollars) a day. Such a situation 'forced' council to consider slashing of maize.[14]

Policy on co-operative cultivation and slashing of crops

The then Minister of Local Government and Town Planning (Mr Enos Chikowore), realising that Harare City Council would soon slash maize, issued a statement instructing the city not to slash maize until council had made sure that the public had been made aware and educated on the matter; thus effectively giving a 'reprieve' on to residents cultivating at the time.[15] This only delayed an imminent process of slashing.

On its part the Harare City Council delayed slashing of maize and for the first time came up with a clearer policy to partly accommodate urban cultivators as well as slashing of crops. Demarcation of areas was carried out again and the new policy was that cultivation of council land could take place on portions of land leased from council by co-operators. Thus it became clear that council was not entirely against urban cultivation, but against uncontrolled cultivation. Council could destroy without notice any crops grown in contravention of this policy.

By the end of November 1985, Council had done more publicity and with a clearer policy it went ahead to slash crops during November and December of 1985 as well as January and February of 1986. This was a new development which became a feature of all years to come. Crops slashed included maize and vegetables while members involved in slashing were from the ZRP, NRB and the Municipality. Each institution had a role to play during the slashing operations. Their duties during the operations were as given on Table 6.1.

Table 6.1
Duties During Maize Slashing Operations, Harare

Department or section	Responsibility
Town Clerk Municipal Security Unit	for leadership on security
Department of Works (Amenities Division) DHCS	were doing the slashing
(District Officers)	identified the illegally cultivated area and provided maps to assist those slashing
ZRP	security and protection
NRB	as observers

Early responses to maize slashing

Responses to urban maize slashing in these early days were in favour of council action. Councillors in Glen View (where some maize was slashed) fully supported the action. The people (residents) reported that they were fully aware of council policy and few complaints were received. Residents mentioned however, that in future maize and vegetables just outside their stands should be spared.

Commenting on the slashing a responsible officer in the DHCS reported that slashing exercises had gone very well and they demonstrated that:

"Council does not always bark, but can bite . . . But in future it should be necessary to: (a)have enough slashing personnel so that the exercise

94

is completed in a very short time. (b) now that maize and vegetables have been slashed, it is essential that grass cutting be speeded up. Otherwise residents would not see the relevance of slashing their maize whilst grass which is the breeding home for mosquitoes is left to grow".[16]

The last comment is worth noting since in latter years residents used it to argue against Council action on maize slashing. Council has continued to slash vegetables on private property leaving tall grass all over. Slashing of maize continued in all years after 1986 with few conflicts reported. For the urban residents, co-operative organisation became a vehicle to access urban land for cultivation. All seemed well until the Mabika case of 1989.

The Mabika case and beyond: 1989–1992

In the post 1986 period especially 1989 into the 1990s, Council has strengthened its resolve to slash maize grown illegally on council land (prohibitive measures). Well documented cases in this regard are the Mabika case of 1989 and the 1991 slashing. In January 1989, municipal employees invaded and slashed maize and vegetable crops in Mabvuku, Tafara and Chishawasha. Residents interviewed reported having cultivated in some of the areas for decades adding that hunger was the main reason why they cultivated. In February of the same year (1989), municipal teams extended their operations to the western high density areas. Workers slashed 12 hectares of almost mature maize in Mufakose. The response from the public and the cultivators on this occasion were of shock, outrage and contempt of Council action noting that the maize slashed in Mufakose belonged to a co-operative.

Realising the negative impact this "overzealous" action would have on urban governance, council instituted investigations which resulted in the dismissal of the then Senior Town Planner Mr W. Mabika who was among officials spearheading the maize slashing operations. About a year latter he was reinstated on full pay.[17] In 1989, after the Mufakose maize slashing, Council lamented that its image had been tarnished. Yet in 1991 it was back at it; slashing with renewed vigour. A number of observations are worth noting in this period.

Firstly the 1989 Mabika case showed that there was no central authority responsible for decisions on slashing thus leaving loopholes for the Councillors to manipulate the situation in their favour. Secondly, the professionals alleged that housing projects were delayed or shelved as a result of maize cultivation hence the slashing. Thirdly, in both 1989 and 1991, municipal workers slashed crops and vegetables which were on private property and on land not susceptible to erosion. Commentators questioned on the motives of this behaviour. Fourthly,

Council compensated those co-operative cultivators whose maize had been slashed. Observers have a couple of unanswered questions on this aspect. Where does Council get money to pay slashers and then compensate the victims afterwards? Could this money not be put to better use in the first place?

Fifthly, while Council slashed maize, tall grass harbouring mosquitoes featured in all areas. Municipal services of water, rubbish/refuse removal, health services, ambulance services and accommodation were at their lowest level ever. The Sunday Mail (29th December 1991 p. 5) summed up 1991 as the year of critical shortages. With such a background, residents questioned Council's priorities and motive in slashing maize.

The slashing of crops was further questioned in 1991 and 1992 when the whole country, crippled by a devastating drought, has experienced food shortages and resorted to food imports. With the food security in mind, all maize slashing was suspended for 1992. Those who believe in supernatural powers allege that the 1992 drought was partly a punishment from God for destroying gifts given to the people. Food should never be destroyed.

5. Concluding observations and insights

Uncontrolled urban cultivation is a socio-economic development of significance to poor urban residents. The chapter had a simple objective to establish whether institutional responses to off- plot urban cultivation are prohibitive or accommodative. Harare's responses are sporadic, ad-hoc and unplanned. It is not an accommodative authority. Responses to managing urban agriculture are diffuse and ad-hoc. This is not helped at all by a highly departmentalised system of local government where horizontal analysis and attack of common problems is non-existent. Yet to simply describe it as prohibitive may not be enough or appropriate. It could be best described as an 'arbitrary authority'. The bulk of the presentation provided historical material of a descriptive and informative nature. It could be of use for other arguments beyond concerns of this chapter.

Responses to urban agriculture in Harare have not always been prohibitive. Prior to 1985–86, Council pursued a publicity policy where it tried to educate people on bad effects of urban cultivation. This failed to stem the tide of urban cultivators. From 1985–86, Council adopted prohibitive measures in the form of slashing maize. This has received bad publicity in subsequent years than the accommodative approaches. Commentators and the public have attacked this approach on moral and humanitarian grounds which has drawn attention away from the earlier accommodative council programmes as well as the real opportunity costs arising from urban cultivation. Alternative means of survival for the urban poor have to be made available if the residents are to completely stop cultivating urban lands.

There seems no chance of halting urban cultivation given its economic value to urban residents. Council has to continue controlling the activities in general and accommodating them where possible. In this process Council has to inform the public more than hitherto. Such information should highlight not only negative impacts of urban cultivation, but how to do proper urban cultivation. In addition the opportunity costs especially that relating to potential housing lost or delayed should be made known to the public.

The information distribution should also be part of the whole local authority's *image* campaign which should highlight not only Council's positive programmes, but emphasise on the role and responsibility of urban communities to manage their own environments. Council has to demonstrate emphatically how urban cultivation is a threat to the environment especially the threat to siltation of rivers and urban water supplies.

Accommodative approaches are still possible but are made complex by a number of factors which include the cost of staging education campaigns and monitoring exercises. This cost is however present even in the prohibitive scenario. In pursuing accommodative approaches, the co-ordination of Council activities needs to be streamlined. On paper the linkages, channels of communication and responsibilities are clear. What is not clear is the question of who should make and implement critical decisions such as the decision to slash maize.

The role of Councillors in these programmes need continuous attention since these (councillors) change quite frequently. It takes time for new incumbents to understand and correctly interpret council policies. While in the mid 1980s they were on the fore front to assist in educating the people, it seems of late they have used urban cultivation as a political weapon to get votes. It appears that in some cases councillors have allocated land for urban cultivation contrary to procedures of the Local Authority while some have not supported council professionals in implementing decisions. When maize is eventually slashed, such a situation breeds more confusion on the part of the electorate while in general it portrays a local authority in disarray.

Urban agriculture in Harare (and Third world cities in general) is a challenge in both management and research terms. Acknowledging its persistence, ubiquity, productivity and value to urban economies, heightens the need for research with a focus on:

a) removing obstacles to urban agriculture and enhancing its stake in the urban economy.
b) how to promote urban agriculture without compromising on environmental quality and aesthetics in the urban areas.
c) urban food production and nutrition systems with special emphasis on the urban poor.
d) cost-benefit assessments of urban agriculture with special reference to opportunity cost of land utilisation.
e) integrating urban agriculture with health and waste management variables
f) access to land and equity issues in the production and distribution process with special reference to the gender dimension.
g) financing and control relationships on the activities at household and institutional levels (i.e. NGOs, government and community levels)
h) urban economy theories that recognize the importance of and incorporate urban agriculture in both its spatial, social and economic dimensions.
i) policy options that maximise benefits from urban agriculture without compromising on aesthetics, service provision and urban governance.

In responses to urban cultivation in Harare, there is also a case for a serious review of centre-local relations in terms of making laws and effecting them. For practical purposes, there is also need to critically examine and streamline departmental responsibilities and levels of control within the city council, based on a clearer policy on urban agriculture.

Notes

1. Illegal cultivation, stream bank cultivation are other terms used to describe this activity.
2. The Finance Committee, The Planning and Works Committee are examples.
3. For example the Department of Works, The Department of Housing and Community Services and The Department of Health.
4. Concerns were for soil erosion on cultivated areas and the subsequent siltation of rivers and dams which would arise from this; noting that Harare is in the catchment area of streams which drain into major dams supplying water to the city. These are to the south west of the city within a 35 km radius

5. A central government department currently falling under the Ministry of Environment and Tourism
6. DHCS A/45/71: 25 th January 1982
7. DHCS A/45/7: 11 March 1982
8. See The Herald, 15 June 1982, Harare
9. Local language spoken by at least 75 percent of the population in Harare
10. A major river draining south east of the country. It is heavily silted with soil eroded from communal lands in the catchment area.
11. DHCS A/45/7: 2 nd August 1982
12. For details see The Herald, 5th December 1989 and DHCS A/45/7/185
13. The Herald, 16th November 1982, page 3, Harare
14. For further details, see The Herald, 6th September 1985, pp1, Harare
15. For further comments on the matter, see: The Herald 8th January 1985 p.1, 9th January 1985, p.4 and 19 th January 1985, pp 5, Harare.
16. Details are given in DHCS A/45/7/115, 26 th February 1986. It should be noted that elsewhere in the country, urban maize crop had been slashed in Marondera Town resulting in residents staging a demonstration against Marondera Council and demanding financial compensation (The Herald, 29th December 1984 p. 3) while in Masvingo Town, five thousand gardens were reported destroyed in January 1985 (The Herald 15 th January 1985, p. 3)
17. Four years latter in 1993, Mr W.N Mabika was elevated to the post of Deputy City Planner, Harare.

7 Urban Agriculture in Zimbabwe: Testimonies of Women from Warren Park, Harare

" People used to laugh and scorn at urban cultivators. In these years of economic hardships, everybody wants to have a piece to cultivate. But land is not enough. You see all those houses? They have walls and roofs.....but there is nothing left inside" Mai Achimwene, a cultivator providing an economic justification for the upsurge of urban cultivation in Harare, 1992.

1. Introduction and research questions

The objective of this chapter is to review gender dimensions of informal urban cultivation with respect to how actors respond to opportunities and constraints in the urban environments. Such a focus is desirable in that it centralises a neglected social sector — women. The bulk of urban unemployed peoples are women and their proportion is even higher in urban agriculture. The phenomenon is considered as trivial pastime work for housewives and recent urban immigrants. There is need to be informed by cultivator testimonies. The chapter highlights the needs, problems and experiences of women's double burdens of production and reproduction. The material provided can be useful for those debating conceptual issues such as breadwinner, household , household head e.t.c.

A number of issues were reviewed using findings from cultivation in Warren Park high density area of Harare. It is observed in the chapter that contrary to common belief, urban cultivation does not benefit the poorest of the poor. Access to cultivation land by the poor is made difficult by factors which include informal 'gate-keeping' relationships among early urban residents. Although women dominate in the sector, men do participate in a number ways.

Despite the observed dominance of women in urban agriculture, no protracted attempts have been made in terms of research to analyze or give insights on women's life as urban agriculturalists. As assessed by Freeman (1990:18), writings on African urbanisation have propagated opinions which view urban cultivation as an 'unimportant pastime indulged in purely by city housewives'. There is a vicious cycle which trivialises both urban agriculture and women's economic contribution in general. Examinations of women's oral presentations have not been used to inform scholarly research and urban policy.

While attention to urban cultivation and women may thus be justified and is important, it must however be remembered that it does not tackle the basic problem of women's access to education, skills, wage employment and more lucrative opportunities for self employment, and therefore should only form one part of a strategy designed to improve the position of women in the urban system'.

2. Searching for methods

As illustrated in chapters two, three and four, urban cultivation in Harare covers almost all areas namely open spaces in high density (low income), low density (high income) residential areas, industrial areas, roads and railway reserves, slack land and land reserved for future built development. Ideally one would be inclined to select a sample representative of each category of broad land uses. The main constraint has been resources to cover all these strata.

At the sampled area level, the problem is to get a reasonable sample of cultivators to work with. There are problems in that there is no known population to sample from. Secondly the plots they cultivate are neither uniform nor well delimited. At times communal type cultivation is practised. Thirdly there is no period during which one can find all households or cultivators on the plots.

Whereas work has been done and is ongoing in various centres in Zimbabwe, this chapter presents insights from Warren Park, a residential area to the west of the Harare city centre. It was in this area that the first interviews with cultivators were conducted incorporating detailed open ended discussions with individual respondents. The researcher interviewed 'off-plot' cultivators found on the spot at any time of the day. The work was done over the period mid September 1992 and September 1993. Cultivators are normally in the 'fields' in the mornings and late afternoons. On Sundays the majority prefer not to work.

The disadvantage in this exercise was that at any point early in the morning, there would be many cultivators. It was not possible to capture all of them since a lot of time had to be spent talking to one cultivator. To get along with the cultivators it was found necessary to go at a slow pace making sure they were comfortable with the researcher before asking detailed questions. Often the cultivators are harassed by Council Officials and reported in the press. It was essential therefore to distinguish clearly the differences between these other professional dimensions from the research under way. The cultivators had questions to ask as well and these had to be answered satisfactorily before proceeding to the next cultivator. This presentation does not discuss issues relating to 'on-plot' cultivation; a matter which is the subject of chapter 4.

3. Insights from cultivator testimonies

Methodological insights

Cultivation is of several types. First is cultivation on dry land and rain fed. Around September there is no such cultivation since no rains will have fallen. However such land was under preparation; clearing and burning of old season crop stalks[1] Ploughing was also done by hand or by tractor

Second is Cultivation on wet land which is prone to flooding during peak rain season. Around September at the peak of the dry season, such land is moist enough to support maize and 'madhumbe'[2] crops. By September cultivation is already in progress such that the crops will be ready for harvest in December (i.e. early part of the normal planting season).

Cultivation is also in riverine areas were there is water in the streams. In such instances watering of crops is prevalent. Vegetables are dominant crops though maize is also grown. It must be noted that the water is not from purified municipal supply systems.

One can see that for a detailed study, all three categories need analysis in addition to the spatial detail noted at the beginning. Cultivators also vary. There are those who cultivate on demarcated zones (legal zones) as co-operatives or as individuals. Then there are those who cultivate on land beyond the cultivation limits — the illegal category. Thus a comprehensive view would have to capture cultivators from each of these categories. It was not possible yet to say how many cultivators there were in each category or how large a sample to take.

Urban management literature accepts that cultivators are dominantly women and children. In Harare women cultivators are in the majority; about sixty percent of cultivators. Men participate as contract labourers or as assistants to their female spouses. From the many men encountered during the surveys, testimonies will be provided from those whose responses were quite graphic and typical. Names used are labels and not the true names of the cultivators.

Man number one, Tengo Mosikeni, was a foreigner of Mozambiquean origin. He was digging land as part of preparations for the rain season. Of interest in this case was that the man was preparing land on contract as an employee of a woman landlord and paid Z$20.00 for digging a piece of land 20 m x 30 m. " I get a lot of customers. This is the best time for me" he said.

He was not willing to release details of his residential address although he was prepared to give that of the woman land lord. Thirdly the piece of land under preparation was in the illegal zone. To this aspect he responded thus:

> "I cannot read, but I know what the signs mean" referring to city council notices advising residents not to cultivate in that particular area.

Two other men in a similar category i.e. employed on contract, could be pointed at in the vicinity. Unfortunately they could not be captured during the time available.

Men number two, Dick Mafuta, was cultivating in the illegal zone as well. But this piece of land was close to a flowing water course and he was watering his crop of maize beans and vegetables. This was a different case in that he was employed at Olivine Industry as a general hand and was off duty on this particular day. He had his family with him; two boys and a girl in their mid teens. Referring to the tough economic situation resulting from the 1991-1992 drought in combination with effects of the Economic Structural Adjustment programme, he lamented:

> *"Handisati ndamboona shangwa yakadai"* meaning " I have never seen such a desperate situation as this"

He has been resident in Harare for over ten years and was allocated a residential plot in Warren Park during the early 1980s. In all these years he had not had as tough a life as in this year so he resorted to urban cultivation. Although the wife was not available on this day it was she who worked on the plot most of the time, he said.

Man number three, Mufundisi Pachuru whose rural home is Masvingo Province of Zimbabwe was cultivating a plot leased to him by a woman landlord. This piece of land was on dry land (anthill in particular) located in the 'legal zone' It is leased to unemployed church members of the Apostolic Faith sect to which the woman landlord belongs. This man had been cultivating with his male partner on this piece for two years.

"The piece is given to our unemployed church members to keep them busy during the day" he explained.

The landlady was said to have been allocated a residential plot in the Warren Park area in the early 1980s. Both had plots in their rural homes.

The oral presentations highlight social and economic motives of men cultivators and perceived benefits from the activity. Generally the survival motive is paramount. They also inform us on cultivator views on official policy towards urban cultivation in Harare. In the next sections, these testimonies will now be complimented with those of women cultivators to get not only the overall picture of cultivation issues but the gender contrast as well. The survival motive is common to all cultivators although differences exists in how members actually participate.

Aliens image

Cultivators include a significant proportion of people of Malawi, Zambia and Mozambique origin. These are descendants of labourers who came to Zimbabwe (then Rhodesia) during the colonial years to work on mines and commercial farms and as domestic workers. These jobs were at that time shunned by indigenous Africans. A lot of aliens have lost contact with their home communities and due to economic constraints cannot go back. Some were born in Zimbabwe and intermarriages with locals are common. But both the formal and informal land allocation laws exclude these people from owning land in the rural areas. As a result, the bulk are in urban centres where in order to survive, they get into informal sector activities including urban agriculture.

In this survey, Mbuya Kapoto was the first alien to be encountered. She was an old women who pretended to be mentally disturbed. She was preparing land in the illegal zone. Of interest was the fact that she had been cultivating different-plots every season. She claimed to be of a Malawian origin (Vechirudzi[3] as she put it) but was not able to go back. Her grand-children are Zimbabwean citizens. Assisting her on the plot was her daughter-in-law who was visiting from the Chiweshe communal lands (about fifty kilometres north of Harare) and a contract

105

male labourer whom she claimed to pay $50 for digging a 60 m x 60 m plot.

Mbuya Kapoto was allocated a residential plot in 1981 in Second Street near the Warren Park Police Station. She could not be convinced to give her full address or her name. At the time of survey, her husband worked for Zimbabwe Electricity Supply Authority (ZESA). She summarised her economic position thus:

"I have nothing. In good years I keep chicken, this year I have nothing"

Rural urban linkages

Urban residents still have strong ties with their rural communities. Mai Chivi migrates to Harare to join her husband during the dry season and goes to the rural home during the rainy season to cultivate the family plot there. The husband was allocated a residential stand in the early 1980s and was employed in the formal sector. Her story has two important points. She used to cultivate a plot in the Kambuzuma residential area of Harare. But when residents in that area got into cultivation as well, all non-residents were flushed out.

"I lost out when I went home. On coming back, all people from Warren Park area could no longer cultivate in Kambuzuma area. Everyone came here. Since I was absent, I could not stake a claim" she explained

Consequently, she was now cultivating on a piece of land in the legal zone leased to her from a woman neighbour who allegedly had more than one plot. Her daughter was assisting her and would do the rest of the work during her time away in the rural area.

The "co-operatives"

Tauya Agricultural Co-operative is one 'women only' co-operative in Warren Park. This co-operative had a total of ten members cultivating a 2 acre plot. They all were allocated residential plots in the early 1980s. All were preparing their portions of the co-operative plot with the assistance of their children (school going age). Each would cultivate a well defined plot of about 40 m x 30 m. In all cases they were able to narrate the history of urban cultivation and the procedures followed by Co-operators. They could tell who their councillor was at the time of allocation of land. Like all her colleagues, Mai Samanyika was keen to elaborate on the Tauya Co-operative;

"We are members of Tauya Co-operative, yes, but we cultivate individually . . . we formed our group in 1984 and got this piece from the Department of Housing and Community Services. . . At times we share costs to hire a tractor to plough our land" she explained.

There was neither co-operative work nor use of resources most of the time. Residents like Mai Samanyika accepted the call to form co-operatives in the mid 1980s only to facilitate access to land. Beyond that level, it is difficult to say a co-operative existed.

Motives and problems of urban cultivators.

In all cases tough economic conditions in the urban areas have forced families to seek extra means of survival. The opening comment by Mai Achimwene is just one of the many expressions given to summarise economic hardships faced by urban residents in Harare. Cultivation supplements food reserves in the homes and provides the option of not buying vegetables and fresh mealies from the market. Residents used to ridicule urban cultivators, but now it (the activity) seems to be the envy of everyone. Many who would like to cultivate cannot get pieces of land. Land available to cultivators is not enough for them. One of their problems is getting inputs for their cultivation activities.

Gate keeping and entry into urban cultivation and the urban poor

Urban cultivation seems to be a closed industry; restricted to old city residents. Those who got pieces of land in the early 1980s have somehow stuck to those pieces. They can only be cultivated by someone else on a lease basis. Therefore it would be difficult for a newly arrived urban immigrant to get a cultivation plot in Warren Park. The implications are that urban cultivation may not be for the poorest of the poor. The poorest are the unemployed, those without houses of their own and without a rural land to plough. The poorest of the poor in urban areas include those households headed by women. These were not identified as cultivators from the surveys.

As the testimonies revealed all the women had homes which their families owned and the household heads (husbands in this case) were in formal full-time employment. In good rainy seasons they have options to cultivate in the rural home. That they have own homes implies that they could have a space for use for home based crafts and small vegetable gardens. Others may sublet some of their rooms thus getting some income or have their rates paid from rents paid by lodgers. Even without lodgers the mortgage rates for houses allocated in the early 1980s are far lower than what a resident would pay as a lodger in the same area. The cultivators in this case are already better citizens than the poorest of the poor. However, since they are mainly women the poverty issue

107

may need to be abstracted from a family level to the individual levels in terms of how much control women have on outputs from the activity.

Who in the family decides and makes decisions on urban cultivation

Women control and make decisions on whether to cultivate or not. But the consent or blessing of the husband has to be given in all cases.[4] This is necessary for two reasons. First the husband may be required to assist with finance for fertilizer or implements; in most cases he is the one with access to a formal job and a constant income. Secondly there are risks of coming in conflict with the local authority and the husband would have to account for any eventualities. Only in a few cases do the men actually come to assist in the plots. The majority that do are children or employed labourers.

Urban cultivators and urban policies

In all cases the cultivators were aware of regulations or procedures relating to urban cultivation. Through notices and contact with officers from the Department of Housing and Community Services the cultivators have become aware of their rights and limits. Those women in co-operative groups could provide a lot of detail on the historical development of urban cultivation. Dates and names of council officials responsible were given quite accurately.

Even those cultivating in the illegal zone were aware of this fact. Indeed they could point to the pegs and warning signs put up by the city officials. These signs read *"haparimwe"* meaning "not to be ploughed". But it was a worthwhile risk they said. It would be unfortunate if the maize were to be slashed. From a pro-official position, Mai Janasi a cultivator member of Tomboedza 'Co-operative' warned:- "Red light says stop, so if you cultivate in prohibited areas, do not complain when the crops are slashed"

Maize slashing and tragedy of the commons

Maize slashing is a response the Harare City officials have resorted to in the past. Cultivators felt that if any maize (legally cultivated or not) has to be slashed then the slashing has to be while the crop is young; not when it is almost mature. The danger of land degradation and consequences on water supplies were also acknowledged. But cultivators feel that as families they have to survive and everything else comes later. Thus the 'common interest' which the city officials wish to promote and protect finds itself incompatible with survival strategies of individuals and households at the local level.

There was no clear indicator to establish whether the cultivators try to influence cultivation policy in any way. The women expressed no ambitious to take up political posts as councillors although they participate in the voting process. They seemed satisfied with the existing political set-up.

Concluding remarks — where do we go from here?

In terms of methods, a study of urban cultivation provides an interesting challenge. Quantitative methods would only be realistic in the selection of study zones. But as one goes down to try and isolate the plot(s) or cultivator(s) for inclusion in the study, sampling in its traditional form is difficult to implement.

The type of information required to answer questions and responses to situations is primarily qualitative. The research topic is then an example where qualitative research using observer participant methods, detailed interviews and open ended discussions are the tools.

Urban cultivation is an activity dominated by older urban residents. Entry by new urban immigrants is difficult unless they lease a piece of land from urban land-lords. Contrary to council policy and procedures, urban cultivators 'cling' to their pieces of land. Council requires cultivators to renew their tenure every season and start cultivating only after such renewal.

However, cultivators proceed without renewing their tenure. They seem to be aware of the regulations. Even those cultivating in illegal zones are aware of their position. They take it as a worthwhile risk in their efforts to sustain their families. Where council takes an accommodative and educative approach to the activity, the cultivators are to blame if their crops are slashed.

At the household level, women make most of the cultivation decisions. Consent of husbands is needed in all cases though.

More analysis needs to be done in the sub-categories identified. The internal dynamics at the household level need to be explored further. The same applies to the economic input output analysis of the activity. Research needs to follow up on aspects of multiple plot ownership by cultivators and women status in the homes. It is clear that there is a possibility of landlordism in this activity. In this case, the very poor do not benefit from urban agriculture.

Women are not a homogenous group. There are married, divorced, single parent and single women. Beyond the life cycle status, there are race, religious and class divisions. From the Warren Park testimonies, we observe the existence of 'women landlords' in an area and urban community generally labelled poor-low income.

There is need therefore to go back and revise our generalisations on poor women and women in the Third World. At the city level, there is need to extend women issues and gender studies to high income groups. These are equally affected by the urbanisation and modernisation processes and have in some cases travelled a mile further on the 'transition path'. What experiences and gender contradictions exist in their lives vis a vis their female/male counterparts whose generality belongs to the peasantry?

This chapter has not attempted to provide a monetary value to output from urban cultivation or the quantitative proportion of food produced compared to food purchased from incomes earned by spouses from formal employment. But the meaning and value to the cultivators should be evident. From the testimonies, women are working hard to sustain their families indicating that women's societal roles in urban Zimbabwe are not different from those of their rural counterparts. They have not changed. It has always been a central and pivotal role equal if not greater than that of the male counterpart. What has changed are our notions of women. We have, over generations, ascribed to women images as passive breeders subordinate to men. Western culture, research and domination of Africa by the west has also promoted, directly and subtly, some of these views on the African women. Thanks to gender analysis, women are receiving more of what is due to them.

Notes

1. Maize is the major crop grown on such land.
2. A tuber crop which is prepared like potatoes for consumption
3. A derogatory term used to describe aliens of Malawi origin
4. Consent may even be an inappropriate word since it may not reveal who wields power in the home. Therefore one could explain this relationship from the perspective of power 'inequities' in the home. The term 'inequity' is borrowed from Yvonne Hirdman p. 187-188 where she attempts to demonstrate that the choice of words in gender studies can hide truths and make significant issues appear trivial. However, in a discussion of women headed households, Anita Larson (1992) observed that 'many married women . . . as a rule are supported by their husbands . . .' p. 2

8 Images of Urban Cultivation; Tools or Products?

"The eye is never neutral, and many a battle is fought over the 'proper' way to see" David Harvey (1989: 1) The Urban Experience, Blackwell

Introduction

This chapter[1] is about techniques and concepts in social science. It centralises the role of our impressions of the environment; how they are shaped, how we present them and how they influence the way we operate in that environment. The central technique is photographs and this chapter will attempt to illustrate their value in social science and planning research. It is hoped that the technique will assist in enriching our appreciation of the multidimensional issues related to urban cultivation in Zimbabwe.

But what is social science and planning research? What is the role of photography in this field and how can its value and potential be fully exploited? These are basic questions whose answers should form a common working platform for the stake holders. Once this has been accomplished, the presentation proceeds to the next stage where each participant or reader is granted the opportunity to be different; scanning the photographs, analyzing them and creating mental images about the phenomena of urban cultivation and the social, human, economic and political background it represents. The reader must continue to ask of each of the images:

'what is the meaning of what I (we) see? How does it compliment or contradict the verbal and written descriptions and explanations, statements and theories that we already have? How best can our resultant images help shape institutional action on the phenomena? '

Responses to these questions are expected to be as varied as the number of participants, their experiences and socio-economic rankings.

111

Nonetheless, one hopes that through the promulgation of these differences, one can extract commonalities and use these to construct a cohesive image to substitute the variegated perceptions we may already have.

The chapter outlines the role of photographs in social science research and isolates their residual value which is utilised to illuminate gender issues in urban management affairs. The will of women to survive and their humanhood are often trampled on, abused, mocked or simply ignored by administrators — dominated by men!

The problem is not about images and photographs. The problem is in our ability to understand them and relate them to our values, ideals and action. Our positions on this hierarchy will determine our judgment of photographs and images; whether they are tools or products, illustrations or manipulations.

On social science research and images

Social science is a field of study designed to explore the human environment, human dynamics and their relations with the physical and mythical world. It bridges the abstract arts and the natural sciences — pedagogical abstracts which are rejected by world evidence on a daily basis. Social science is designed to describe and explain the social environment and processes around us. In the process of social science research, one is faced with the problem of method — empirical and abstract. One has also to contend with the problem of theory; how to generalise and concretise the images, descriptions and explanations generated in the research process.

Again the distinctions of theory and empirical components of research are pedagogical. In reality, they are part of one whole which cannot be sustained in the absence of the other. Where do images and photographic images come in?

A reflection on empirical components of social science and planning research may assist us in this regard especially if one considers the nature of human attributes. Some are measurable while others are not. This has led to the development of quantitative methods to describe and analyze those measurable attributes of the human environment. On the other hand is a range of unmeasurable human factors leading to a sub-area of qualitative techniques and research.

Although this too is a pedagogical dichotomy, it is the qualitative research theme that may help us comprehend images as tools and products in the research process. By definition, qualitative research is any kind of research that produces findings that are not arrived at by means of statistical procedures or other means of quantification. It can refer to research about persons' lives, stories, behaviour . . . organisational functioning, social movements or interactional relationships (Strauss & Corbin 1990:17). Information in the process of qualitative research process is gathered by means of interviews and observations, use of records, documented evidence, tapes, images e.t.c. The problem is that by depending on observations, divergence is an accepted eventuality since the same object can mean different things to different people.

On images and social science research

How do we decide and design appropriate methods for recording our experiences, what we see and what we believe in? Photographs, though they may be ambiguous in the information they give can at times be more emphatic than spoken words and written statements. In planning and geographical study, they would be classified as models. And as models, they have been accepted and utilised without question. The classical works of Kevin Lynch (1960) are a good example of how photography and images can be used to both illustrate and translate an idea. Numerous books and documents in design, planning the built environment in general and project planning have accepted use of photography without question — but in the majority of cases using images as an ancillary not the major method. The majority of cases imply an understanding of the objective of photographs. That is where this presentation is different. It attempts to bring into perspective the subject of images before using them as a tool.

Wegner (1979) reminds us that social science research is not the only field where photography has been or could be used beneficially. The police use images in tracing down criminals while our passport and national registration systems are heavily dependant on photographs. Photographs give finality to oral and written presentations.[2] Wegner further records that archaeology, geology, physics, botany, biology, chemistry, astronomy and medicine have all made extensive use of photography in data collection, experimentation and comparative analysis[3] Photography has become an essential and routine tool for research.[4] One may add that modern history and life as a whole would grind to a halt if photography and images were to be removed from the scene. Bring to mind the family albums, personal photographs of childhood days, travels, good and sorrowful moments e.t.c. The newspapers, the television and magazines capture our attention and transmit their messages through photographs.

While photographs' role in social science discoveries is not easily evident, they do have a role and strength in presentation, documentation and recording in 'native format' the social processes as seen by the photographer through the limits of the camera lens. Through the graphic capture of events, images communicate to the reader or viewer in an intensive way. Photography has a further characteristic of recording extra data in addition to that initially intended by the photographer — most of it deemed useful at a latter stage. This is the theme presented by Wegner (1979) when he further explains categories within which social science research can use photography. These categories are:[5]

a) photographs as interview stimuli
b) photographs as a tool for systematic recording of events e.g. traffic patterns at a junction or the stages of a development project.
c) content (and context) analysis
d) native image analysis
e) narrative visual theory

On the other hand Lynch (1960) takes the complementary start point that visual images are an essential means by which we perceive and order the world.[6] This is the basis upon which we manoeuvre in our environment — using perceptions and images, landmarks, corridors e.t.c. Images of the environment as a basis for individual and institutionalised action (planning and design being good examples) is the other facet we take for granted but which Lynch (1960) so perfectly illustrates.

What then about images (photography) in social science and planning research? The foregoing presentations should lead to a synthesis that there seem to be two standpoints for image utilisation viz;

a) images as an investigation and analytical tool, as a data base — a source of records or information which are the inputs to mental image formation.
b) the mental image formed as a synthesis of knowledge gained about the environment which is then the basis for personal or institutional action (Planning) to create and shape the physical environment.

The way forward: more questions

If the above outline captures the value and benefit of photographic images in social science and planning research, how do we proceed to utilise them in research on urban cultivation?

How do we proceed on the sheets of images to follow?

1 what are the distinguishing features of each photograph (what is distinct in the photograph)?
2 what could have been the objective of the photographer who took the picture?

3   how would you have taken the picture to promote the same objective?
4   how can we distinguish that which is contributed by the setting or subject of the image from that which is contributed by the photograph?
5   what information does the photograph portray?
6   with what frequency do certain variables occur in the photographs?
7   would someone else photographing the same phenomena come up with the same kind of photograph?
8   what aspects of the photographs (images) affect you deeply, confirm, reinforce or contradict what you already thought to be true?

A synthesis

Photographs can convey truth and clarity in a situation that is obscure. What is the situation of women cultivators in Zimbabwe? Photographs can also be used as political tools through systematic presentation of part and not the whole of a story. But photographs are also crucial in that they capture events beyond what is intended or realised by the photographer; leading to what one can call the residual value of photography.

Most of the photographs, images in this chapter were produced by different photographers. There is all the likelihood that their motives were the same or very diverse. Trying to establish what agendas they each had could be an interesting PhD research of its own. However, the analysis of the articles' titles and follow ups led to the conclusion that although urban cultivation was explicitly the object of all the photographs, the issue of women or gender in urban affairs was far from the photographers' interests.

Yet it is clear even to the amateur student of gender studies that the photographs contain volumes of residual information on women issues in Zimbabwe. They vividly portray the struggle of women to do something of their own, to survive, to keep going, to keep family and society surviving.

For the student of gender studies, the photographs further reveal the 'hierarchy and domination' relationships that exist between women and institutions of urban governance. Women's engagement in urban agriculture in Zimbabwe is as high and as significant as that of their counterparts in rural areas. The obstacles to progress are enormous in both cases.

These are images of one person — the author ! Biased one could say, and using photographs for some undeclared agenda !

Plate 8.1
Use of open spaces

Infrastructure reserves such as this railway land in Rugare, Harare, are cultivated every year.

Photo source: Author 1993

Plate 8.2
Can this subsistence activity be
converted to intensive commercial

Cde Naume Nyakudya working her plot in preparation for the next rainy
season. Cultivation on these vast open spaces is currently informal and
subsistence in nature. These are spaces where intensive all year round
agriculture could be introduced.

Photo source: The Herald, 31 st August 1992, Harare

Plate 8.3
Men contribute manual labour

Cde Eddison Kamwana and his wife Tabita cultivating the stretch of land dividing low density areas of Bluff Hill and Mabelreign, Harare, while son Collen sucks a freezit. These open spaces are considered too wet and clay for built development.

Photo source: The Herald, 17th November 1993, Harare

Plate 8.4
The map is upside down pal?

Stream Bank Cultivation — One of the major arguments against urban cultivation. Monitoring exercises involve extensive mapping, municipal police patrols, publicity campaigns (through radio, newspapers, field pegs/ notices and meetings with community groups) Is it worth the trouble ?

Photo source: The Herald Picture Library, Harare

Plate 8.5
"Haparimwe" Not to be ploughed

If not used for cultivation, the land remains open veld or is used by the affluent to take walks, as golf courses etc. The cultivators ignore 'haparimwe' and grow food crops.

Photo Source.   The Herald, Harare

Plate 8.6
Any farmer would be proud to have such a crop!

Productivity per unit area is higher in urban areas especially riverine areas.
Cultivation is intensive and the soils are usually moist and fertile.

Photo source: The Herald Picture Library, Harare

Plate 8.7
The way we play!

Contributing to Family Food/Income starts from a very tender age. In another world, these children would be playing computer games after school.

Photo source: The Herald Picture Library, Harare

Plate 8.8
The way we play!

These teenagers are preparing earth mounds on where to plant sweet potatoes locally known as 'mbambaila' or 'mabura'. The land is private property for housing development in the low density area of Mt. Pleasant, Harare.

Photo source: Author 1993

Plate 8.9

Different use of open spaces

Children also improvise and use some of the open spaces for after school soccer. The ball is home-made from plastics.

Photo source: The Herald 2nd November 1993, Harare

Plate 8. 10
Inequalities also exist at the micro level

After school, the 'girl-child' has more chores to perform at home than the 'boy child'. Here memory Munhenga leads her sister Theo (left) and (Tsitsi) Mangisi from Budiriro District Office where residents 'are now collecting water' following a temporary closure of the mains water supply to houses in the area.

Photo source: The Herald, 31 August 1992

Plate 8.11
The 'home front'

Cde Katsunge at his home in Mufakose, Harare. On-plot gardening is done on over 90 percent of properties in the area. Vegetables are grown throughout the year. Advocating for reduced stand sizes in such as areas (USAID and World Bank brokered ideas based on aid for infrastructure supply indicators) is an implicit condemnation of survival activities in the home.

Photo source: The Herald Picture, 4th August 1993, Harare

Plate 8.12
The rich are also in it

Urban cultivation is not exclusively an activity of the poor. Residents in low density areas use large portions of their properties to grow crops for consumption. Here a young maize crop flourishes on one property in Mt. Pleasant, Harare. If we discourage cultivation in high density areas or reduce stand sizes in those areas, what do we do with realities like this one in Mt. Pleasant.

Photo source: Author 1993

Plate 8.13
Men at work

Harare City Council workers slashing maize allegly grown on stream banks in 1989. What a waste — many would say.

Source: Herald Picture Library, Harar e

Plate 8.14
After the slashers — all in vain!

A resident who had all her maize slashed (1989) "bursts into tears". Stream bank cultivation ? There seems to be no stream on this relatively flat piece of land. The maize was nearing maturity.

Photo source: The Herald Picture Library, Harare

Plate 8.15
Unbridled authority?

A resident removing slashed maize from her flower bed just outside her security wall. All flowers planted in the same bed with the slashed maize were left untouched. She was not the only victim. But she rightly asks: "Is this stream bank cultivation? Is this council property ?"

Photo source: The Sunday Mail, 29th December 1991, p. 1, Harare

Plate 8.16
What the hell is going on here?

One man ——ten women—plus a 'men authority'; gender insensitive administration ?. Bitter co-operative women holding cobs from their almost mature 12 hectare maize crop slashed by council workers in Mufakose area. A local councillor is 'told' how the crop was slashed.

Photo source: The Herald, 11th February, 1989 page 1, Harare

Plate 8.17
Women speak out on maize slashing

But are their voices heard? A women resident of Mufakose interviewed after the maize slashing of 1989. "We want not less than Z$700 compensation per member for the maize slashed — and the punishment of the person responsible for the maize slashing" she said. Four years later in 1993, no compensation had been paid.

Source: The Herald, 16 February 1989, page 5, Harare

Plate 8.18
Women speak out on maize slashing

A woman resident of Mufakose interviewed after the maize slashing of
1989. How many of her words do the politicians remember . . . that is if
they ever 'heard' them in the first place.

Source: The Herald, 16th February 1989, page 5, Harare

Plate 8. 19
Women speak out on maize slashing

This woman resident of Mufakose was 'chairperson' of the group whose maize was slashed in 1989. . . her voice as leader of the co-operative was never listened to by the men who were 'doing their job'

Source: The Herald, 16th February 1989, page 5. Harare

Plate 8.20
Women speak out on maize slashing

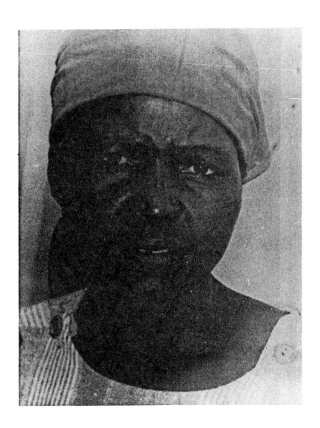

"I was looking forward to selling the maize to earn money to feed the family because my husband is not working. Would council do something about compensating us ?

Source: The Herald 16th February 1989, page 5, Harare

135

Plate 8.21
The suffering majority — women and children!

When water pipes burst and houses go without water, when grass grows tall and mosquitoes breed, and when councils fail to supply refuse removal services, ambulance services, electricity and housing, it is the women and children who suffer. "Is there a lack of understanding of priorities ?"

Source: The Sunday Mail, 29th December 1991, page 5, Harare

Plate 8.22
Urban harvests are reasonable

Yields from urban cultivation are high. Here Highfield area co-operative women joyfully sing as they winnow their maize before sending it to the Grain Marketing Board for sale.

Photo source: The Sunday Mail, 18th April 1993

Plate 8.23
At the grinding mill

Produce is also taken to the hammer mills. More and more urban residents are turning to straight run maize meal and neighbourhood hammer mills are now on the increase. Here men and women are queuing at a hammer mill in Highfield, Harare. Some of them said they had arrived as early as 4.00 a.m

Photo source: the Herald, 4th July 1993, Harare

138

Plate 8.24
Rural — urban linkages?

With the high cost of maize meal, some urban families are now preferring to bring maize from the rural areas which they grind into mealie-meal. In the picture, Cdes Leonard Madziva, Shorai Madziva and their mother carrying some maize they have brought from Nyanga to their house in Dzivarasekwa. A strong sign of rural-urban linkages in the food sector or is it a sign that the rural poor are better off than the urban ? Some petty-traders also sell maize grain at urban neighbourhood shopping centres throughout the year.

Photo source: The Herald, 1st January 1994.

Plate 8.25
Vending for survival

Unlicensed vendors sell fruits and vegetables outside the main
supermarkets at all sub-urban shopping centres giving customers a wider
choice. However most of the fresh vegetable sold here is grown outside the
urban areas.

Photo source: The Herald, 22nd September 1992, Harare

Plate 8.26
More production on the home front

Non agricultural 'home based industries' are vital in up-lifting peoples living standards. Fence making is one such activity encouraged in high density areas.

Photo source: The Herald, 21 st June 1991, Harare

Notes

1. Originally Presented to MA Regional & Urban Planning Participants on/women and Technology Course as a Guest Lecture, Department of Planning and Architecture, University of Nottingham, United Kingdom, 16 March 1993..
2. Plummer (1983) p. 22 describes photography as (a) strategy of conveying immortality upon experiences — a from of surveillance and control.
3. Wegner (19979) p. 4
4. In effect, air photography and air photo analysis form a solid foundation and procedure in geography, land use and town planning.
5. Details of each category are presented on pages 16–19, Wegner (1979).
6. Similarly indicated by Wegner (1979) p. 17

9 Subsistence Urban Cultivation in Zimbabwe: Any Lesssons from the European Garden Allotments?

Introduction

This chapter is an 'experiment' whose aim is to establish whether and to what extent our understanding and perceptions of urban cultivation in Harare can be enriched by a review of the experiences of Europe in dealing with the urban allotment gardens starting from as early as the 19th century. The historical and practical value of urban cultivation in Zimbabwe has yet to be established. On the African continent in general, few cities encourage urban cultivation and Harare the capital city of Zimbabwe is considered in the literature as one of those restrictive cities in its manner of handling urban cultivation. The restrictive approach has been observed as prevalent in Southern Africa, Lesotho being the significant exception. The traditional definition of urban has been based on the prevalence of non-agricultural economic activities in a given settlement. Thus to talk of urban agriculture may be considered a misnomer. Yet urban cultivation especially that of cereal crops in Southern African cities is prevalent and has been on the increase in Zimbabwe. However, there is no consensus as to the value and meaning of urban agriculture hence policy and administrative responses are disparate. Can we learn anything from the allotment gardens experience of Europe?

An answer to this question can only be provided after the task has been attempted. And in handling it, the challenge is to present both cases; that of Zimbabwe and that of Europe and thereafter extract valuables. For Europe, the garden allotments experience of England and Wales between 1850 and 1994 will be used while the case of Zimbabwe is illustrated by details from preceding chapters. On the European scene, most of the information on allotment gardens is archival mainly in reports of committees which were never published for library use. To search for and access such documents requires an understanding of the local languages. This language constraint excludes for scrutiny the experiences of continental Europe; Sweden, France, Germany, Italy, The Netherlands and Belgium. Efforts made in 1993 to search and access some of the documents in Holland produced a handful of documents after two weeks. Then there was the problem of translating the materials from Dutch into English. In the end the exercise proved expensive and time consuming. There is a rich experience in all these countries which the case of the United Kingdom cannot fully duplicate; it is unfortunate that the documents are inaccessible.

The cultural, political and socio-economic realities of the United Kingdom are very different from those of Zimbabwe — now and in the past. Sceptics would therefore be justified in questioning the value to Zimbabwe of gleaning on the European experience. This is an issue discussed in section two of the chapter and commented on throughout in other sections. The objective is not to impose on Zimbabwe what prevails in Europe, but to increase our knowledge by observing origins, developments and reactions to similar problems in a different setting on which our influence is nil.

In subsequent sections, the structural similarities and differences of the two cases are outlined. Since the bulk of the UK's experience is now historical, we are using that experience as 'time data' to increase our knowledge of the current situation. There are issues of interest in terms of land characteristics, cultivator characteristics and the problem of administration. If there is anything to learn from Europe, it is the observation relating to the value and meaning of urban agriculture. This value and meaning is period specific; urban agriculture is generally a response activity to some national economic crisis associated with nation-wide poverty or general erosion of assets. It is this basic realisation which should guide policy responses to the phenomenon in terms of whether to promote or not to promote urban agriculture and the degree of input supply by national and local governments.

To compare is to consider more than one case at a time. In social sciences, sceptics to such an approach as a method of cross-national review would argue that only programmes and policies which are very much alike in style and context can be usefully compared. However, such 'alikeness' and 'usefulness' cannot be gauged before an actual comparative exercise. In comparative reviews, we seek to learn from the experience of the other and identify structural and ideological determinants of social policy, to isolate issues and trends which are general and unique and those which defy time. Among the questions to ask are: what common elements exist in the two situations?; what elements are peculiar to certain time epochs, to certain national or international conditions?; and are any of these elements a result of inter-dependencies which characterise the systems under review?

In the case of urban agriculture in Zimbabwe versus the history of garden allotments in Europe, we are dealing with processes happening at different time periods — almost 100 years. We may focus our attention on determining conditions under which urban agriculture thrives and those under which it will whither away. In responding to this and other questions we have to remember that the history of a society can be understood by reflecting on the way in which members of that society at any period enter into social relations with one another in order to produce their means of existence. Comparisons can also be insightful even across disciplines. For example in a discussion of third world housing, van der Linden (1986) writes that there are many similarities between the allotment garden movements of Europe and the present day self-housing movement in third world countries.

The allotment origins: rural and urban

The European allotment gardens (the UK. in this case) were initiated in the rural areas of England and Wales in response to rural poverty arising from landlessness. From around 1760 and gaining momentum in the early years of the 18th century, a process of rural land enclosure was instituted through Acts of Parliament e.g. the General Inclosure Act 1801 (DCIA, 1969: 2).[1] This process involved the division of areas or open fields and manorial commons[2] into separate parcels which were then 'allotted' to those individuals who could prove entitlement to the share of them. Enclosures also reserved relatively small allotments of land for community use as 'recreational allotment'; 'garden allotment'; 'water allotment'; or other allotment according to purpose (DCIA 1969:2).

Many peasant cultivators found themselves unable to or ill-equipped to prove entitlement on the rural land as richer landlords grabbed and enlarged their land holdings. Thus there emerged from the enclosure system, a rural proletariat and a great social evil, namely poverty.[3] In response to rural poverty thus created, church organisations, the wealthy, philanthropic groups, state institutions, and some landlords supported the parcelling out of small allotments on a charitable basis for use by the poor labourers. Cultivation on these allotments was supposed to be secondary to the labourer's main tasks and responsibilities on the landlord's estate. The allotment was supposed to keep the labourer busy and away from the pub and mischief during his free time.

The objective of this brief background is to indicate the rural origins of the term 'allotment'. When it was brought to the city, it may have referred to a different type of land but the motive was basically the same; that of giving something to the poor. For differentiation purposes, rural allotments will be called 'farm' or 'inclosure' allotments while the term allotment gardens will be reserved for the urban areas.

In a capitalist land holding system, it would not be difficult to find parallels to the above in another country miles away. In Zimbabwe, the term allotment does not exist but poverty, both rural and urban is rampant. With colonialism imposed in the late 19th century, the indigenous black population was alienated from its rural land through treachery, chicanery and military conquest where the former were not successful. These were the foundations to the land problem which is central to the history of Zimbabwe over the last 100 years. Currently, through rural resettlement and land re-organisation programmes, the state is making efforts to respond to the plight of the landless rural folks. Though details of the problem in the two situations may differ, one notes the existence of poverty as a product of social relations in a given population and how that relation facilitates access or in-access to productive resources, especially land. The rural scenario, indeed has a bearing on the urban through rural urban interactions dominated by population migrations, movement of goods, social and cultural variables and power.

The urban poor and the down trodden

Rural economic collapse and poverty for the majority in the United Kingdom coincided with rapid industrial growth of the late 19 th century and early 20 th century. There was consequently a rural to urban drift by the rural land-less in a bid to eke out a living as labourers in the industrial towns. Efforts of rural land allotment could not reverse rural to urban migration and rural depopulation. In practical terms, this process led to a spatial transfer of poverty from dispersed rural areas to

146

localised urban areas. By the late 19th century and early 20th century, various efforts were in place to try and tackle urban poverty in England and Wales. Urban 'allotment gardens' were encouraged as a way of affording the poor labourers and the unemployed some form of productive recreational activity. Philanthropic organisations, the church, private employers such as the railways and mines mobilised resources and supported allotment garden movements. Later, more labourer-based movements took over the bulk of the organisational roles for making land available for some use as allotment gardens. Motives for supporting this phenomenon varied. Generally, it was to stem the urban poverty scourge and also to facilitate adjustment of recent migrants to city life. For some, the provision of garden allotments was an indirect way of shielding workers from socialism. The labour movements and unions also adopted the idea of allotments ascribing to it the goals of enabling workers to earn an extra income, supplement household diets and more importantly reduce the labourer's dependence on the employer. It was further seen as an indirect way of promoting co-operative movements (van der Linden 1986: 42).

In Zimbabwe, the existence of organised agricultural groups in urban areas is not as advanced as was experienced in Europe before the first world war. Some form of co-operatives are formed as a means to get access to land whereas the actual cultivation of plots is done on a very individual basis.[4] In studies on Harare, the link between rural landlessness and urban cultivation was explored. It is urban unemployment and poverty which are the causes rather than mere rural landlessness. Some of the urban cultivators have rural land which they cultivate or could cultivate if they so wished but prefer to stay in the urban areas where most nuclear families now reside. The issue of rural landlessness is slightly different when we consider aliens. Aliens are Zimbabweans of foreign origin; namely those originally from Malawi, Zambia and Mozambique who came to Zimbabwe to work on mines, commercial farms and as domestic workers during the colonial period when indigenous Zimbabweans found it repulsive to take up this type of work and even to work for the white men in general. After several generations there is now a significant population of these aliens most of whom have been firmly integrated through intermarriages.

To a great extent, these folk are excluded from rural land ownership. Both traditional land allocation systems and the modern statutes on land do not provide for aliens to own land in the rural communal areas. As documented in chapters 3 and 4, up to 37% of cultivators in the Harare were identified as aliens and for them, lack of access to rural agricultural land was posed as a reason for cultivating in urban areas. Indigenous Zimbabweans have seriously taken up cultivating in urban areas only recently; from about 1989. Therefore putting current economic conditions aside, lack of access to rural land does contribute to the need for urban cultivation in Zimbabwe as it was for Europe in the 19th and early 20th century England and Wales.

External stress, urban food demands and nations under siege

The motives for accommodating allotment gardens or urban cultivation have varied in sympathy with national circumstances and prevailing socio-economic and political pressures. This is vividly evident when a review is made of allotment gardens in Europe during and after the World War years, and the period in between especially the Great Depression of the 1930s. These are the periods when events fuelled the growth and entrenchment of allotment gardens.

Available literature shows that by 1913, there was a keen interest for allotment gardens in all urban areas of the United Kingdom; 'every man a garden' was a common campaign then. The outbreak of the First World War 1914 to 1919 gave impetus to the extension of urban garden allotments (DCIA 1969:16). Food provision became a national priority and urban civilians were called upon to contribute to the survival of the nation both in terms of industrial productivity and food supply during the war. The DCIA (1969: 16) reported that :

> "In December 1916, local authorities were invested with powers under The Defence of The Realm Act to secure as much land for the provision of allotments as exigencies demanded. Immediately, every small piece of open space including parks and play fields and traces of undeveloped building land were requisitioned; parks superintendents offered advice and assistance; an intensive advertising campaign even door to door was set in train"

Authorities assisted with seeds and implements and fencing was done whenever required. Private organisations such as the Railways, The Coal mining companies all encouraged allotment gardens and made some of their land available for the "Defence of The Realm". After the first World War, demand for allotment gardens remained high as returning ex-servicemen needed something on which to survive. The demand was maintained high with the setting in of the Great Depression in the 1930s when unemployment was again very high. The role of allotment gardens was considered so significant that during the inter-war years, a flurry of legal, administrative and institutional provisions were made in their favour. The allotment Act of 1925 for example required consideration of garden allotments in all town planning schemes and regulated that land purchased or appropriated by local authorities for allotment gardens 'must not be disposed of or used for any other purpose without ministerial consent'. In detail, section 8 of the act reads:

148

"Where a local authority has purchased or appropriated land for use as allotments, the local authority shall not sell, appropriate, use, or dispose of the land for any purpose other than use for allotments without the consent of the Minister of Agriculture and Fisheries after consultation with the Minister of Health and such consent . . . shall not be given unless the Minister is satisfied that adequate provision will be made for allotment holders displaced by the action of the local authority . . ."

A similar display of national purpose was repeated during the Second World War and after when there was a pressing need for food production at home. Therefore allotment gardens were of military, political, economic and cultural value. The DCIA (1969: 20) reports that in a November 1947 national broadcast, the Chancellor of the Exchequer stressed the importance of allotment cultivation as a contribution towards the solution of the United Kingdom's economic difficulties while the then Minister of Agriculture declared in 1948 that:

"Today we are digging for our very lives, for food, for dollars and for our self respect"

The United Kingdom was a nation under siege; a situation which demanded resource mobilisation at all levels in the country and motivation through campaigns such as 'Dig for Plenty' of the 1940s and 'Defence of The Realm' of the First World War years. Map 9.1 is an extract to highlight how urban allotments in the Birmingham metropolitan area flourished in tandem with national socio-economic events including the world wars.

There are a handful of insights for Zimbabwe from this experience; the most significant of which is the national motive. When national need is defined and goals set, the activity of urban agriculture can become meaningful. In order to provide food to sustain the economy during the war years and preserve national pride, the United Kingdom found allotment gardens useful. A similar situation prevailed in Zimbabwe during the peak of the 1991-92 drought. Although not as grand as the United Kingdom's situation, during those years in Zimbabwe, local authorities were given a Ministerial directive not to discourage urban cultivation; in particular to refrain from maize slashing as in the previous years. On humanitarian grounds, and food security reasons, the nation had to get food from whatever source possible including urban cultivation. Since the drought years, there has been an unprecedented growth in urban cultivation activities by women, the unemployed and even well to do families. Whereas food may be abundant nationally, the national economy is in limbo; many households have a money supply scarcity, hence the need to supplement their resources from

Map 9.1
Changes in distribution of allotments, Birmingham 1885–1965

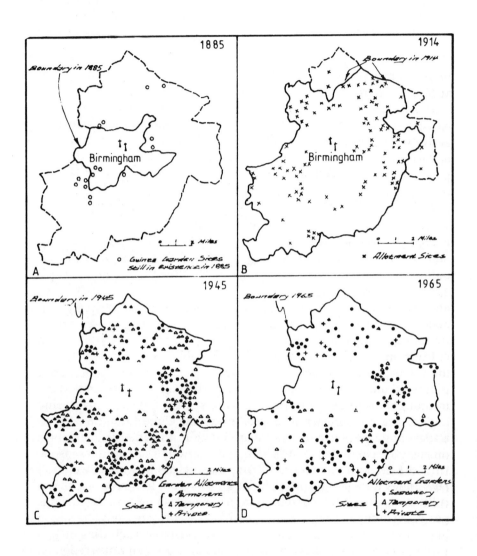

Extract from page 9 DCIA Report 1969

whatever source possible. Instead of buying all their food from supermarkets, urban residents can save some cash for other uses by cultivating their own food on urban open spaces.

Authorities in Zimbabwe have not taken a solid position on urban cultivation since the 1991–1992 drought. The question to ask is whether Zimbabwe should consider its national economic conditions as an adequate excuse to promote urban cultivation. Once there is general agreement on this question, experience shows that it may be possible to mobilise resources including expertise for the management of urban lands and involvement of the private sector. While the United Kingdom mobilised 'parks wardens', Zimbabwe would need to mobilise land use experts, agriculturists and environmentalists to assist and guide the activity so as not to compromise the sustainability of the urban environment. The result of such combined operations and oneness of purpose could include increased food supply and productivity of land better managed than that in the rural areas.

The introduction and role of town planners is also crucial. The United Kingdom experience demonstrates that the role of these professionals is only positive and less ambiguous in a well-defined political, social and problem environment which is understood and appreciated by society at large. Such a congruence of understanding and problem appreciation by society and its leaders is a condition not always present and heavily lacking in urban affairs management in Zimbabwe today. As long as there is no political and social consensus as to the value of urban cultivation, the initiatives and role of town planners on urban cultivation will be viewed negatively. Possibly, their best option is to 'do nothing' about urban cultivation at this stage. Alternatively, town planners should seek for a political resolution before they can act technically. Being politicians themselves is an extension to this option.

The case also illustrates that as an issue of national interest, an understanding has to be reached between central and local governments on how, by whom and how to handle the activity of urban agriculture. In Zimbabwe at present local authorities seem not to have any framework for handling urban agriculture or seem incapable of utilising the little legal backing they have. There is a fragmented and diffuse line of responsibilities to Ministry of Environment and Tourism, Ministry of Local Government Rural and Urban Development, Co-operatives and Employment Creation and The Ruling Party ZANU(PF). In the end nobody seems to bear the final responsibility and everybody manipulates urban agriculture to suit themselves when conditions demand. There are many casualties in this process, including the environment.

The influence of environmental conditions on the status of urban cultivation is further illustrated by the fate of allotment gardens in England and Wales during the late 1950s and 1960s; a period when Europe was free from wars and experiencing increased economic growth. Prosperity and affluence became a characteristic of Europe; better wages and social benefits for the unemployed became a norm thus obliterating the need for urban workers to supplement their incomes or food from urban gardens. Cultivation of allotment gardens became economically unattractive. Refinement of refrigeration technology allowed for bulk storage of fresh food, fruits and vegetables; again relegating the need for an allotment garden. As a recreational activity, the allotment garden could not compete against new forms of outdoor and indoor recreation including the TV. A general interest in allotment gardens nose-dived and plots became derelict or under-utilised.

After the Second World War, Europe went through a period of massive reconstruction and rehabilitation characterised by urban expansion and an increased demand for land in industry, commerce and housing to accommodate increasing urban populations. Available land found priority use in new areas of town planning and built development. Allotment gardening became a luxury in this new era. Therefore at both the household and national levels, the need for allotment gardens declined such that allotment plots were absorbed by other urban land uses or where they persisted, they were neglected and under-utilised. Under these circumstances, town planners found no resistance to their plans which carried proposals for use of allotment plots for built development. Further, the rent paid by allotment gardening could not compete successfully against high value urban land uses such as housing, roads, offices, industry and commerce. Land use was allotted to the highest bidder such that the poor were squeezed out to make way for capital and the middle class.

There is one succinct lesson for Zimbabwe arising from this scenario, namely the need to isolate epoch specific values of urban agriculture. It has to be emphasised many times over (for the benefits of both the antagonists and protagonists) that the activity of urban agriculture in its subsistence form has played and can play its economic role under specific national conditions. For Zimbabwe, the possibility exists that it could be playing a role in sustaining households during tough economic conditions. Once the decaying economic conditions have been reversed, cultivation would die a slow natural death. Or it would possibly remain as an activity of sentimental value to a few nostalgic individuals; that is moving from a 'rescue' activity to a 'recreational one'.

At the peak of their existence, allotment gardens had some characteristics which those in Zimbabwe may find interesting to look at. These relate to plot size, acreage, crops grown, implements used and accessibility by the urban population. It has already been mentioned that the urban labourers, generally the poor had reason to demand a garden allotment. The definition of poor, varies from society to society and even in a given society, it is a relative condition. However, in urban Zimbabwe, as long as those in Harare claim they cultivate because of perceived economic conditions/hardships, we can take their situation to be similar to that prevailing in Europe about 50 to 150 years ago. There are also similarities in the location of allotment sites which were, as in the Harare case close to the homes or workplace of the cultivators. The basic fact being that urban cultivation requires the 'least cost' situation and minimum time wastage in order to be viable. Secondly, such proximity would allow or allows complementarity of the activity with other domestic or work chores without disruption of the latter.

In Harare the average urban cultivation plot is about 400 square metres (not regular in shape); a size which tallies well with that of allotment garden plots in England and Wales which were 300 square yards or a quarter of an acre and below (DCIA 1969: 15 and 16). Incidents of multiple plot ownership i.e. situations where one individual had ownership or access to more than one plot were recorded in England and Wales. This feature is also prevalent in Harare.

Ownership of the cultivation land is a fundamental concern in this issue. Like in Harare, the majority of allotment gardeners, did not own the land they cultivated. This land belonged to the local authorities, the state, the private sector or individual landlords. The difference is that those in Harare are not paying any land rent to the local authorities while those in England and Wales paid for the allotments.

There is also the issue of acreage at city level. There is no agreement on exactly how much land in the cities was put to use for allotment gardens or how many people were actually involved at any point in the history of the activity. Estimates in Harare put the proportion of cultivating households at 19% in 1993, 42% in 1994 of the total population in Harare while the amount of physical space actually cultivated is between five and ten thousand hectares. This varies from year to year and seems to be on the increase since 1989. At the peak of allotment gardens in England and Wales between 1914 and 1919, the highest proportion of households with access to allotment gardens was estimated at 22% for urban areas (DCIA 1969: 16). Although the figures are close to those of Harare, they show in both cases that the majority of urban residents have no access to this resource. How can this majority be persuaded to support a cause in which they have no direct benefit?

For researchers in Zimbabwe, it may be encouraging to learn that figures from Europe are estimates made from information compiled from various sources. The DCIA (1969) report laments on the inadequacy of accurate records of allotments in England and Wales. Available information was complied using a variety of methods (conflicting at times) in sympathy with whoever was presenting a case for or against allotment gardens. The question to ask may be whether a knowledge of exact quantities is necessary in the case of Zimbabwe and to what use such quantities would be put. Answering this question could assist in deciding whether we need to waste resources mapping and measuring the spatial extent of urban cultivation and if we do, what methods to use.

Plate 9.1
Stanley Road Allotments, Sheffield

Stanley Road allotment; intensive agricultural use of open space close to a new residential area.

Source: Sheffield City Council, 1994

Plate 9.2
Meersbrook Park Allotments

Meersbrook Park in the south of Sheffield is the largest allotment site in the city. Flowers and vegetables flourish. Note houses in the background.

Source: Sheffield City Council 1994

Plate 9.3
Plot 48 Meersbrook Park Allotments

Inspecting flowers and vegetables on Plot 48, Meersbrook Park allotments.

Source: Sheffield City Council, 1994

Plate 9.4
Public, community and private sector patnerships

Competition Time! Leisure gardens competitions are organised by the city
council with financial assistance from the private sector.

Source: Sheffield City Council, 1994

Plate 9.5
Everybody is welcome

Allotment award winner at 1993 competitions, Ronald Chrouch grows sweet and cayenne peppers, pumpkins, hot chillis and marrows at his Skye Edge allotment.

Source: Sheffield Telegraph, Friday 13 August 1993

Plate 9.6
Security of Tenure?

Len Harding (70 at 1993) at his allotment off Sharrard Road, Sheffield, picked as the best in Sheffield for 1991, 1992, 1993 competitions; has been working the plot for 30 years.

Source: Sheffield Telegraph, Friday 13 August 1993

In contemporary Europe, allotment gardens or what used to be allotment gardens, have found a new but different lease of life after their relative neglect in the 1960s and 1970s decades. Rejuvenation has come from the *'ecology'* enthusiasts whereas in England and Wales controversy still persists as some developers and urban planners view allotment areas as under-utilised land which could be put to 'more productive built development'. As in the past, both mid city and fringe allotments still exist and are cultivated by urban residents who in many cases are organised into informal allotment societies.[5] In Sheffield for example, the societies are affiliated to the Sheffield Allotments and Home Gardens Federation which is recognised by the city council. Seeds, fertilizers, weed-killers and gardening sundries are made available to members at reduced prices through these societies. These societies assist in making by-laws for the allotment areas under their jurisdiction. For example a common rule is one prohibiting the keeping of livestock. Applications to keep chickens are not uncommon but are turned down in the majority of cases while the keeping of bees has been accepted as an exception (through some form of special consent) because bees have an ecological role to play as agents of crop pollination (although they can become wild and sting neighbouring cultivators at times).[6]

We have to note that the local authority remains the land owner in most cases and allotment holders continue to pay rent, currently an average of between £12.00 to £26.00 per year per two hundred square metres plot in the Sheffield area. But there have been changes as well. No longer is the activity a survival strategy for the low income people. Professional and middle class people take the activity as a hobby and although all ethnic groups are involved in allotment gardening, people who live in flats or houses with small gardens are the main participants.

Produce is for home consumption or is used for display at recreational agricultural shows. For example pigeon keeping and leek growing remain strong in mining areas in the north-east England. Allotment gardeners compete in growing the vegetable leek; the winner is the one who can grow and exhibit the longest leek.[7] For some middle class people, it gives them satisfaction to eat 'fresh' vegetables from their own backyards.[8] The feeling of self sufficiency and of 'going back to the soil' is a pleasant one for some. In Sheffield the city council runs annual allotment competitions with the support of private companies.[9] Further support is given on themes such as organic gardening, use of green houses, community responsibility and council regulations. At a national level, the green movement would like to see more open spaces in cities treated as ecological lungs not just for the benefit of a few species but as an essential component for the very survival of human beings.

This scenario has its counterpart in Zimbabwe where the affluent members of our society view urban open spaces from a sentimental survival point of view as opposed to the basic need survival of the poor members. This creates a complex problem for the urban managers who in the majority of cases are conversant with one and not both of the two viewpoints. Planners for example are accused of being too obsessed with providing open spaces as 'ecological lungs' and ignoring the survival needs of the poor. A coming together, coexistence or ability to accommodate both concerns is what Zimbabwe needs at this point.

Critical insights and messages

Comparative reviews are, like images, very selective. Depending on what appears critical to the observer, they highlight certain points at the expense of others which may be hidden to the observer or which the observer may consider trivial or may deliberately try to conceal in the first place. This chapter, like its predecessors, cannot claim any purity on this score.

But it can claim to have shown the validity of the hypothesis that under similar conditions of economic relations, societies can experience the same type of problems. There will however be differences of magnitude, extent and the type of prescriptive policy responses. With as much as 150 years difference on the development scale, Zimbabwe's urban cultivation situation seems to have some common elements with those of the urban allotment gardens of Europe, especially England and Wales. Similarities have been noted in the characteristics of actual plots; the sizes, their subsistence nature and socio-economic status of the cultivators.

A recurrent question which needs resolution is what value we should attach to urban agriculture and how to interpret it within the framework of urbanisation processes. With respect to labour, there are two recurring positions on this issue. The first position gives urban cultivation a potential to increase the labourer's independence from the employer thus putting viability of the employer's enterprise at risk. On the other hand, by growing their own food, the workers depress their own wages; they sell their own labour at a lower price. In situations of labour scarcity the reverse could prevail.

In Zimbabwe, the second argument was used by colonialists as a basis for paying African labour wages below the economic rate. It was argued that because the African labourer had access to cultivation plots in the towns and received food remittances from the rural communal home where the rest of the family lived, he could actually survive on a lower wage. This thinking was insulting to the African labourers and nationalist politics used it to attack urban employers during the struggle for Zimbabwe's independence.

In the first argument, there could be validity in Zimbabwe except for a slight difference arising from whom among urban residents actually cultivates. Not all cultivators are employed. Except in the low density areas where cultivators are dominated by domestic workers, the majority in other areas are unemployed family members, women and children (Mbiba 1993). Literature on England and Wales does not bring this out and concentrates on labourers. However, if some family members are engaged in the activity, they do supplement[10] their folk employed in the formal sector thus reduce the family's dependence on formal wages and cushion it against effects of galloping commodity prices.

The third view is that proponents of urban agriculture are only romanticising an activity which burdens labour/workers without giving them much benefit. It considers that workers have to rest at the end of the day instead of straining themselves further after a gruelling eight (8) hour working day.[11] Considering that some cultivators in Harare are unemployed, this may not be a strong argument except in the case of domestic workers who cultivate early in the morning before going to work, over lunch hour breaks, at week ends and off days.

Interpretation is another issue to be resolved. This revolves on what is urban and whether urban agriculture is an urban activity. As presented elsewhere, for example Glass D.V. (1935: 1–30), although early urbanisation meant dominance of non-agricultural activities such as trade and industry, its genesis and sustenance depended on food abundance from the regions. If urban is a way of life, such a view may be too deterministic. Instead, urban is whatever people do in a given settlement. The social processes give character to the city's physical outlook. The later should not predetermine the former. These conceptions need further critical consideration backed by an analysis of ideologies, history of urban development and the way people think.

A more comfortable interpretation is the one which concludes that subsistence urban agriculture is a temporary[12] time-specific urban activity. Prevailing socio-economic conditions in the national economy determine the extent of urban cultivation. It is the same national environment which will determine the perception of 'value' attached to the activity by a society as well as the response to it. Subsistence urban agriculture can therefore be understood primarily as a reversion to a universal propensity to, given availability of open spaces, providing household food resources under conditions of decaying economies. Where a common or general crisis prevails in a society, and once the role of the activity is defined at all institutional and political levels, there seems to be a 'life' for it. In the absence of such comprehensive collusion of perceptions, the activity of urban cultivation assumes a controversial status. The ambiguity under these circumstances makes its management difficult.

This review underlines the fact that town planning and urban management cannot be divorced from the political and social process in any given context. Those who view the town planning profession in terms of 'design', 'operations management' or such other terms need to re-adjust their bearings. Perhaps and as indicated earlier, urban managers and planners need to take economics, politics and urban sociology more seriously.

Notes

1. DCIA Report also known as the 'Thorpe Report' after Professor Harry Thorpe who was chairman of the Departmental Committee of Inquiry into Allotments set to task in 1965.
2. The lands on which medieval peasants could grow crops or graze their livestock on a manor; see Chapter 2, The Manor and Its Cultivation in Bennet H.S. (1956) Life On The English Manor; Study of Peasant Conditions 1150–1400 Cambridge University Press
3. *Other processes did contribute to poverty in both rural and urban areas e.g. the guild system, the wages and pricing regimes, the machine age e.t.c. An outline of these is given for example by Smith N.J. (1972) Poverty In England 1601–1936.* Harper and Row Publishers Inc.
4. Details in chapter 7 of this volume
5. *Sheffield City Council has about 66 operative allotment sites with a total of 3, 357 plots. This excludes sites that are privately owned. In the U.K. as a whole, there are about half a million allotments; one for every forty households.* Information Sheets, Allotments Office, Recreation and Leisure Department, Meersbrook Park, Sheffield City Council
6. Discussions with a middle class allotment gardener, Meersbrook, Park, Sheffield 1994.
7. Discussions with an allotment gardener, Meersbrook Park, Sheffield 1994
8. *Terms such as 'leisure gardens' have at times been used as substitutes to allotment garden under these circumstances. Urban fringe allotments have been upgraded to 'chalet gardens'* (see Hardy and Ward 1984: 262–264)
9. See page 17 of the Sheffield Telegraph, Friday 13 th August 1993.
10. Who supplements who? It appears we should start to consider formal employment returns as supplement to the 'informal incomes' since the bulk of household survival is now from informal 'do it yourself activities'

11. Adding commuting time, the total working day is as high as 11 hours for the low income labourers whose residential areas are located at the periphery of the cities.
12. Yet all developments, like fashion, may be considered temporary.

10 Urban Agriculture as a Counter Productive Activity: Evidence from Harare

Introduction

The literature on urban agriculture acknowledges that this is the largest informal activity in the urban areas in terms of members employed. It is seen as a source of essential nutritional foods for women and children a major way of waste recycling, pollution reduction and a way of keeping the city green at very low costs.

Most significantly for urban management is the question of under-utilised or 'idle' urban land. Proponents of urban agriculture argue that in addition to all the food and employment benefits the activity is a viable and profitable interim use of idle land. Use of idle land does not have to be permanent or long term. Where land is suitable for development of the urban 'built environment' then its use should be on a temporary basis.

This chapter seeks to illustrate that while the benefit of urban agriculture are acknowledged, viewed from the dimension of urban housing provision the activity has been an obstacle. The costs incurred due to housing projects delayed could well be over and above the perceived benefits. City Councils have tried in the past to promote and give a framework for urban agriculture as an interim use of future development land[1]. Problems arise in that this is a short-term activity — most urban uses are permanent or long term. Conflicts arise when the short-term activity has to make way for the permanent use such as housing.

167

There is competition for the common resource land. For housing its availability has to be synchronised with that of other resources or inputs as depicted on Figure 10.1. This is the reason why planned land can go vacant for a number of years before construction of houses commences. The question we have to ask is what are our priorities in the urban areas? Are we prepared for example to lose opportunities for housing in favour of subsistence urban agriculture?

This chapter will proceed to present the magnitude of the housing problem in Harare, concluding that no opportunity should be lost in trying to alleviate the housing shortage. In the third section it will present a case study of housing opportunities lost as a result of urban agriculture.

The case study should give proponents of urban agriculture some evidence to re-think their position. In most cases, the urban managers are seen as very restrictive and anti-urban agriculture. But what are the responsibilities of the cultivators? Should we focus entirely on urban agriculture or try and reverse the economic downward trend which erodes family incomes and promotes urban agriculture? The Harare City Council has something to offer in this regard.

The housing shortage in Harare: a brief

Demand for housing in Harare has continued to outstrip housing supply. The demand has been fuelled by increased rural to urban migration especially to Harare, where people hope to find employment. Supply on the other hand has been constrained by lack of finance, land and building materials. Using Harare City Council's waiting list there were 80 000 families without housing in the city in 1991. This has been growing at an annual rate of 17% since then. Assuming an average family size of 5, then up to 400 000 people have no housing in the city. Because of limitations of the waiting list system, this is a conservative figure.

A more appealing indicator is the lodger, ie a person or persons who are renting a room or rooms in the main house of the landlord or some backyard shack prepared specifically for that purpose. Accurate figures for lodgers are not available, but there are figures for the backyard shacks in some parts of Harare.

The proportion of stands with shanties ranges from 9% to 60% (see Table 10.1). In residential areas under construction, one could argue that these are temporary shelters for the developer. But for old residential areas such as Tafara, this is evidence of the inadequacy of shelter in the city. Not only are these shanties creating a health hazard due to overcrowding, they are also a potential fire hazard built so closely together.

Figure 10.1
The markets for housing

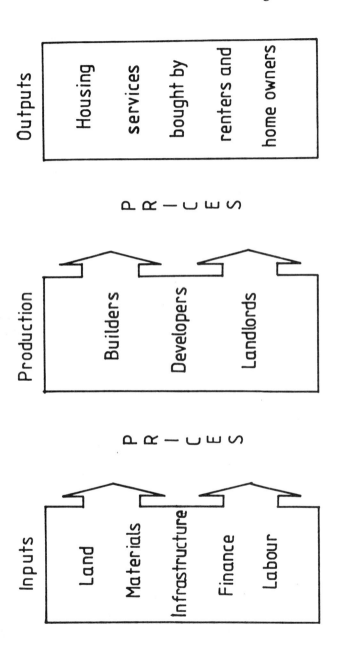

In attacking problems in the housing market. Governments often intervene directly in production and manipulate prices. In many cases they would do better to improve the markets for inputs.

169

Table 10.1
Number of stands with shanties by area

(a) Suburb	(b) Total No. of stands	(c) Stands with shanties	(d) (c) as % of total stands
Glen View	8 663	2 402	28
Highfield	9 991	982	10
Mabvuku	5 983	554	9
Mbare	5 913	707	12
Mufakose	7 632	816	11
Tafara	3 317	1 901	57

Source: *Page 15 — Annual report of the director of housing and community services 30.6.91 City of Harare*

Meanwhile the supply of housing has been shrinking over the past decade in terms of housing stands made available for allocation (see Figure 10.2).

Within this context one would expect residents and city officials to take up any housing opportunity that comes along. The Budiriro case gives a different picture altogether. My hunch is that the downward trend in availability of serviced land for housing has nothing to do with physical land itself but with the deteriorating local government budget overall. In terms of urban economy therefore, as an urban manager, one would want not only to respond to issues of community subsistence, but to have these communities contributing to local authority finances or at least minimise their demands on these decaying budgets. Housing, ambulances, water supply (cholera free water), electricity, refuse removal, health and education services are, in the context of Harare, more worthwhile users of local authority resources than urban agriculture from a public sector point of view.

Budiriro phase 3-5 housing development

Budiriro residential area in the south — west of the city is one of the most recent extensive housing development schemes in Harare. Part of this development was financed by the World Bank. These developments follow a simple procedure which seeks to maintain individual title to land/property holding. Surveying of the lands, provision of infrastructure (roads, water, sewer) are a precondition to allocation of stands and house development.

170

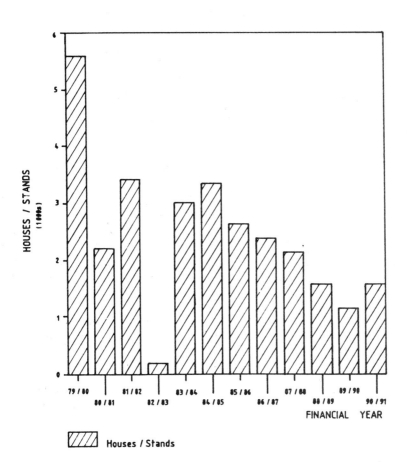

Figure 10.2
Houses/stands made available for
allocation in Harare,1980–81

HOUSES / STANDS (1000s)

FINANCIAL YEAR

79 / 80   80 / 81   81 / 82   82 / 83   83 / 84   84 / 85   85 / 86   86 / 87   87 / 88   88 / 89   89 / 90   90 / 91

▨ Houses / Stands

SOURCE: Annual Report of The Director of Housing and Community Services. 30 / 06 / 91. City of Harare.

In 1990–91 the land surveying task in the Budiriro Phase IV scheme could not proceed due to the presence of maize crops on the development land. Where land surveying had been done, the cultivators had uprooted the survey pegs making it difficult for the City council to provide infrastructure without re-surveying.

The Director of Housing and Community Services in February 1991 reported to council that there was no development in the following areas owing to illegal cultivation which council condoned.

Budiriro Phase 3	1 099	stands
Budiriro Phase 4	1 274	stands
Budiriro Phase 5	3 653	stands
Borrowdale 1	101	stands
Total	6 127	stands

For two consecutive financial years 1989-90 and 1990-91 the council could not develop these stands. Despite the legal provisions in council by-laws which provided for council to destroy without notice any plant, shrub, bush, flower, vegetable, fruit or crop grown in contravention of the by-laws, no destruction was done. Instead, formal publicity channels were used to appeal to and discourage residents from cultivating on this land. All was in vain. Come February 1991, the city council was in a dilemma. The Director of Housing and Community Services reported thus;

> "what is of great concern to us is the fact that the Agreement between our Government and the World Bank expired on 31st december 1990; with room for extension for one year only. This means that Harare has up to 31st December 1991 to have surveyed and serviced Phase 5 which is a mammoth task. Failure to have utilized the Z$19.8 million by end of December 1991 will mean that the City loses the money completely. It would not auger well for the City to fail to use such finances and yet it has such an acute shortage of housing. Because of illegal cultivation, the land surveyors have not commenced any work in the area"[2].

The cited report is an illustration of the frustration experienced by technical professionals in the process of urban management. The public that benefit from cultivating open spaces is the same public which frustrates housing development efforts[3]. The question one may ask is whether these cultivators are aware of the opportunity costs arising from their cultivation activities. In the Budiriro case, housing for up to 6441 families was temporarily held back such that on final provision, the cost would be much more than the original Z$19.8 million.

A number of challenges are thrown up for the proponents of urban agriculture. In the first instance the Harare City Council is not as 'blatant' as previous evidence suggests. There are official programmes to maintain dialogue with potential cultivators and clear procedures to be followed by those wishing to cultivate. At the same time there are plausible arguments of a technical and financial nature for council to destroy crops on urban plots. The challenge is in this case thrown back to the urban communities. Do communities realise or are they aware of the missed housing opportunities as a result of urban cultivation? It is really worth the trouble?

In the strict sense of urban development, agriculture is not a priority activity. It is just an informal response to diminishing opportunities in the formal economy. The challenge for urban managers is that of strategies in the long term. Should urban managers incorporate urban cultivation as a long term urban land use? If so what production system should it follow: subsistence or commercial? Is it commercial, what would this imply for the urban poor?

Secondly, a choice has to be made in terms of re-establishing the economic viability of urban areas. Urban agriculture has no chance of revitalising these economies if it is retained in its current subsistence form. The option is to commercialise it. This implies opening it up to investors who can maximise food production in the cities.

The other challenge is to find broader options of revitalising urban economies through non agricultural industries. This has a more long term permanent impact on development of societies from agricultural subsistence cultivators to modern traders and manufacturers — a development state we all aspire to reach. In this regard the home industries strategy of Harare is a good experiment. This involves making available serviced land for small industries within walking distance to residential areas thereby reducing the constraint of obtaining industrial land by the poorer entrepreneurs.

The evidence from Harare challenges the view that urban agriculture is a panacea to economic ills of the urban poor. It indicates that while some may gain from the activity, a significant number are disadvantaged through delays in housing projects where cultivation acts as an obstacle to land surveying and provision of infrastructure. Some may argue further and say that promotion of urban agriculture in its subsistence form is not only an acceptance of the decay of urban economies in Africa, but a promotion of that decay. It will not help in reversing the downward trend of these economies. If long term economic development is what we desire then the current thinking on urban agriculture has to be revised.

Notes

1. Before cultivating, residents should: identify pieces of land, organise themselves into co-operatives and then approach the city council's Department of Housing and Community Services to get permission and assistance where necessary.
2. Report No. 8/91, A/45/7 Director of Housing and Community Services, Harare City Council.
3. However, as noted in previous chapters, cultivators already have housing or are assured of somewhere to stay in the city.

11 Sewage Effluent Based Urban Agriculture in Harare: Potentials, Linkages and Constraints

Introduction

One of the messages in previous chapters is that urban agriculture in its subsistence form, has little to offer as a strategy to alleviate the decay of urban economies. It has also been illustrated that the activity as currently constituted and practised could be counterproductive, is an administrative burden, an environmental liability and a cost to the urban local authorities.

The objective of this chapter is to review the possibilities of commercialising urban agriculture as a way of increasing its role in the urban economy. Initially, the theoretical possibilities are outlined. This is followed by a review of the current scenario in Harare focusing on how sewage effluent has been used as an input into urban agriculture as a way of assessing the potentials therein. Currently, the city councils in Zimbabwe have the monopoly to utilise sewage effluent to irrigate farms. The economic question to be reviewed is whether such operations can be expanded through incorporation of community participation or joint ventures with private entrepreneurs in the city.

Farming potentials: A general view

Given the high land rents within urban areas and the urban periphery, agriculture has to transform itself to be more productive in order to pay for this rent as well as provide profits for the investor. Otherwise it has to give way to commercial and industrial uses. The transformation of agriculture is possible through intensive use of space; multiple cropping in a given year and utilisation of modern methods of farming. Intensive farming in rural areas abutting urban cores is common; the Japanese and Chinese situations are often quoted in this regard.

Intensive use can also be enhanced by irrigation of arable lands. This is pivotal in Zimbabwe where the rainfall pattern has two distinct seasons. Instead of using water from the dams for irrigation, there is potential to expand and use sewage effluent. Sewage effluent discharged from sewage works can be used for grazing, cattle breeding, fish farming, poultry and horticulture on small holdings. Currently fish farming within the region is done on lake Chibero, Lake Macllwane and Lake Robertson. This could be expanded, intensified and complimented by fish farming on smaller ponds. In addition to effluent, selected refuse from industries could be used in these farming ventures as feed for pigs, poultry or as compost manure on the arable agricultural sector.

Sewage installation works in Harare: background and extent

The bulk of Greater Harare water borne sewage systems drain into the main river valleys of Marimba and Mukuvisi. Some areas of the city (those low density areas in the north and north east) have individual sceptic tanks. The first sites for the current sewage network were established at Crowborough in 1957 and at Firle in 1960. Upgrading and expansion of these facilities has been an ongoing process. The largest sewer treatment works and associated farms are displayed on Map 11.1

The older facilities were based on biological trickling filters which do not extract nutrients from the sewage and this implies than the effluent is rich in organic matter. On this basis and in order to prevent pollution of the river systems, council adopted the idea of pumping this effluent onto farm land which would utilise the nutrients thereby 'cleaning' the effluent before run-off into the river system.

Recently, several Modified Activated Sludge (M.A.S.) systems of sewage treatment have been built at the main sewage works and these remove nutrients in addition to the oxidising process so that the final effluent can be discharged into the rivers.

The increasing flow of sewage from Harare has necessitated an increase in the treatment facilities and in order to avoid regular purchases of land and to use re-generated water, Council has built three M.A.S. treatment plants.

Map 11.1
Sewage effluent irrigated farms,
Harare Metropolitan (south west suburbs)

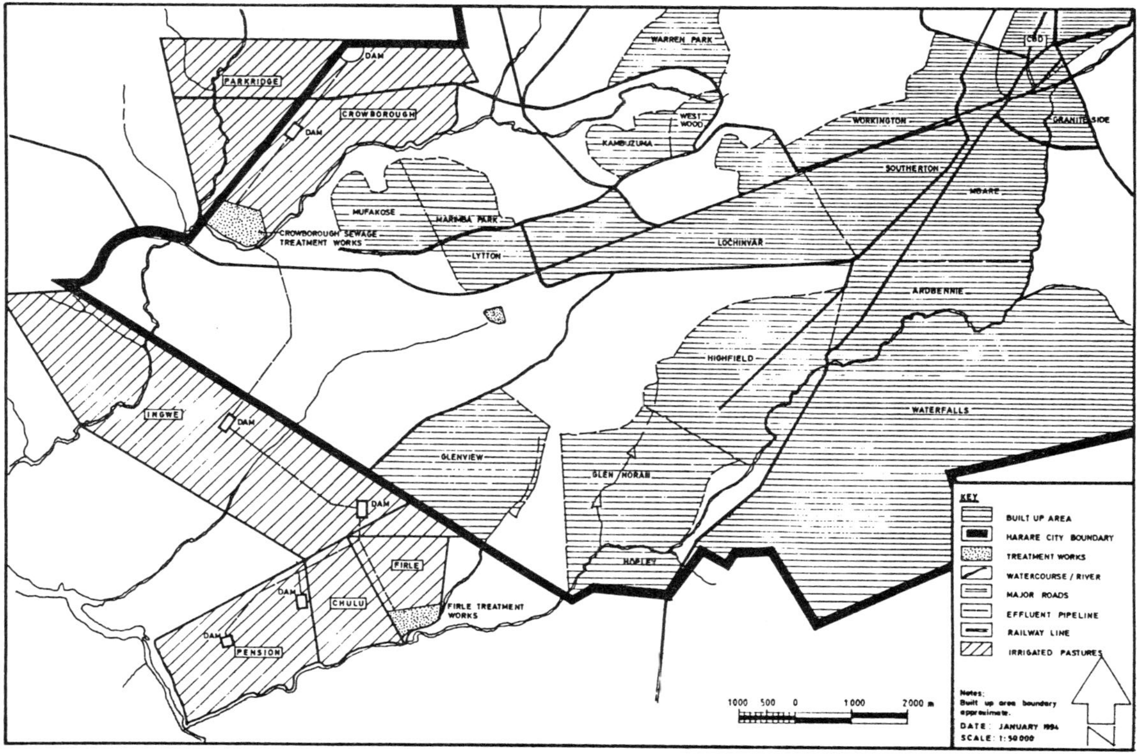

Crowborough works

These were commissioned in 1957, initially to serve the Mufakose Township. They were latter expanded to serve the whole of the Marimba Valley which drains the western areas of Harare. The works have a dry weather flow (D.W.F.) capacity of 36 mega-litres per day (36 ml/day) through trickling filters while the M.A.S. unit treats an extra 18 ml/day.

Firle works

This is the central treatment facility for the whole of the Mukuvisi drainage area. It was designed to handle a D.W.F. of 36ml/day through tricking filters and the treated effluent is pumped into Firle, Ingwe and Pension Farms. Another 36 ml/day is treated by two Modified Activated Sludge Units and the effluent goes to the farms or direct into the rivers.

Pollution control

Pollution of river water is central to council's policy on sewage effluent disposal primarily because of the down stream location of the dams which supply water to Harare. Before improved systems in place today, effluent input into the river systems was nutrient rich. The eutrophication of Lake Chibero in the nineteen sixties was partially caused by the nutrients in sewage effluent flowing into the lake thus providing an ideal medium for algae growth. The eutrophied water was more expensive and difficult to purify. In addition the aesthetic qualities of the water also deteriorated.

Initially therefore, council decided to pump the treated sewage effluent on to land in order to have the nutrients removed by land treatment via pastures. Five farms are now used for the irrigation of effluent. Also a new variable light water intake tower was constructed in the lake, facilitating the intake of cleaner raw water.

The farms and rivers in the catchment and downstream of the sewer network are monitored by the Ministry of Water Development and by Council's Chemical Laboratory in order to ensure that the stringent Pollution Regulations are being observed. The Hydro-Biological Research Unit of the University of Zimbabwe has done analysis of the 'diet' of lake Chibero over a number of years revealing that for the period 1975 to 1980 for example, there has been a reduction of over 80 % in the nutrients reaching the lake from the Harare area. This nutrient inflow is also responsible for the successful fishing industry on the lake. However in the past decade, slackening in the management system led to overgrowth of the water hyacinth which at one point threatened the whole river and water supply system.

In the absence of a 'technology' to purify the effluent, council decided in 1972, to irrigate the effluent on farm lands thereby remove the nutrients. Originally arable cropping tried maize, wheat and lucerne. The yield in dry seasons was considered good, but control of pollution of crops was poor especially during wetter seasons.

In 1976 council responded by moving away from arable to pasture farming whereby the effluent is used to irrigate pastures and fodder crops. The policy has been evaluated as very successful in terms of income, yields as well as reduction in pollution of the final output. Other farms not originally on this scheme have been incorporated to expand the pasture area under effluent irrigation. These farms include Cleveland and Hatcliffe Estate.

The Hatcliffe Estate is considered unique because it is the first of Council's Income Generating projects and is being used to grow crops as well as produce cattle. In the 1984–85 season, 85 ha (eighty five hectares) of maize was grown with an output of 7 (seven) tonnes per hectare. In 1985–86 season the hecterage was raised to 150 (one hundred and fifty) and output rose to 7.7. (seven point seven) tonnes per hectare. In the drought of 1986-87 the output fell to 6 (six) tonnes per hectare and since then has been fluctuating between seven and six tonnes per hectare. Records show that there has been an increase in the quantity of effluent from the housing estates creating a need to bring more farm lands and pastures under effluent irrigation.

The general scenario on the farms is provided in the tables below. These provide summarised information on farming operations; land available, crops and grasses irrigated and livestock as at the 1991 financial year (Fig 11.1 and Fig 11.2).

Table 11.1
Quantities of effluent (Cubic meter per day)

	Average dry weather flow	Average wet weather flow	Design flow
Crowborough works	50 000	80 000	54 000
Firle works	70 000	120 000	72 000
	120 000	190 000	126 000

Figure 11.1
Farm typology and land available

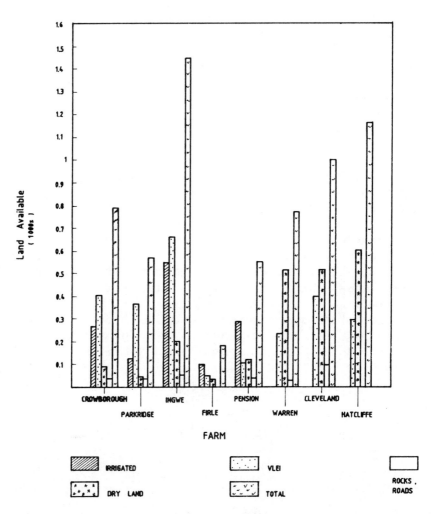

SOURCE : Original statistics from Amenities Department , Harare City Council.

Figure 11.2
Pastures composition on farms,
Harare City Council, 1992

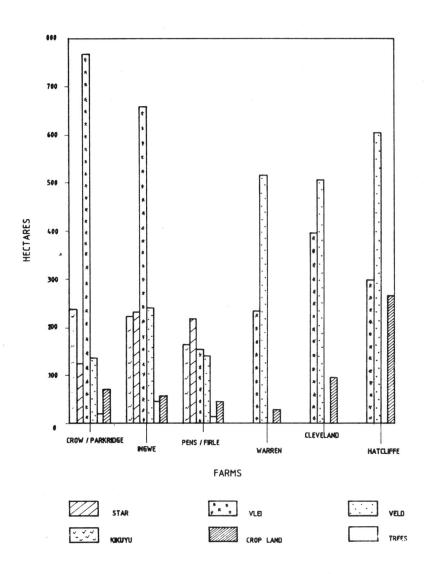

SOURCE : Original statistics from Amenities Department . Harare City Council.

The cattle policy is to breed and sell steers off grass plus a small supplement at about two and a half years during the highest priced months of January and February and cull cows for sale mainly in January/February and May/June. Surplus heifers are sold any time of the year.

Summary conditions of Crowborough and Parkridge farms

The Crowborough and Parkridge farms are run as one unit. On these farms, the soils are heavy clays and are used mainly as kikuyu grass pastures. Tremendous problems have been experienced with kikuyu grass from bloat as can be seen from the bar graph below (Figure 11.3). Star grass has given no problems from bloat and all new pastures for the 1992–1993 years were put down to star grass. A herbicide has been used to kill the kikuyu grass on two paddocks before replanting with star.

The pastures are flood irrigated about every week with no extra fertilizers. A breeding heard of about 1 00 females is run at the moment using beef master bulls. The lush pastures would seem to be ideal environment for cattle but they are also an ideal incubator for pests and diseases and expensive control measures are essential to keep cattle in good health.

Summary conditions on Ingwe farm

This is a sandveld farm which receives effluent from both Firle and Crowborough works and tends to bear the main burden of excess effluent in the summer. The pastures are half kikuyu and half star. Here, kikuyu grass gives much better results than that on heavy soils, both in cattle weight gains and the absence of bloat. There are insignificant nutrients in effluent to give maximum production from pastures on sandveld and star grass has been invaded by 'sporobolus' and other weeds to the detriment of its carrying capacity. Recently sludge has been pumped with the effluent in order to increase the fertility of the sandveld pastures. On this farm nearly 1 000 (one thousand) breeding cattle graze being bred to hereford and beef master bulls in a cross system.

Summary conditions on Firle and Pension farms

These are two sandveld farms run as one unit. All irrigable land has been planted to either kikuyu or star grass. There are 900 (nine hundred) breeding cattle mainly of the sussex breed and are being bred to Sussex and beef master bulls in a cris-cross system.

Figure 11.3
Bloat statistics on farms

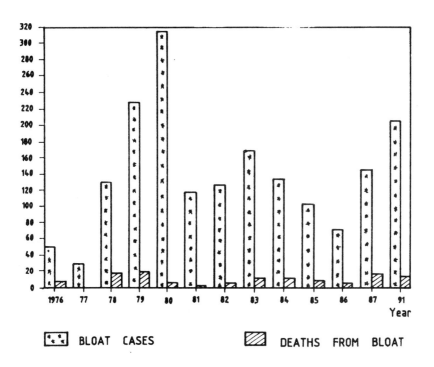

Original data from Harare City Council , Amenities Department.

This farm was purchased for future housing estate development and parts of it have already been put to built development. It is therefore used temporarily for farming and fixed farming investments are kept at a minimum. Before purchase, the lands were farm lands. Young stock are grazed on this farm for a few months before further fattening for slaughter.

Other farms

These include Cleveland and Hatcliffe Farms. Cleveland area is now being grazed by young stock in order to alleviate fodder gaps. On the Hatcliffe farm, during the 1991 season, 700 ha of maize was grown here and 700 (seven hundred) cattle grazed. Further development is held up by unavailability of equipment.

Concluding remarks

The city of Harare was reluctantly forced into farming operations in order to ensure that the nutrients from sewage effluent did not move into the neighbouring streams and lakes. Originally arable cropping was tried but many pollution problems were found such that in 1975 council decided to commence breeding of beef cattle on effluent irrigated pastures. This cattle and pastures policy has paid dividends. In addition, the effluent irrigated farms employ up to 150 workers (Figure 11.4)

The pollution on lake Chibero is minimal and improved considerably from 1975 to 1980. The recent increase in water pollution and weed growth is due to many factors, not related to farming operations of the city of Harare only. It is estimated that the cleaner water in Lake Chibero is saving the City about Z$750 000 (seven hundred and fifty thousand Zimbabwe dollars) in water purification costs.[1]

The farms are generating cattle sales of two and a half million dollars per annum. In addition the cattle herd increased in value by Z$4 000 000 (four million dollars) giving a gross income of over Z$ 6 000 000 (six million dollars). Thus there are gains in costs savings on water purification as well as returns on farming investments.

It is considered that the farms will have to be retained indefinitely because despite the new M.A.S. sewage treatment systems which will permit direct discharge of treated effluent into the rivers, council cannot afford to scrap its huge investment in the existing conventional works overnight. In addition the phosphates removed by the M.A.S. process come away as concentrated waste activated sludge and this will have

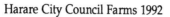

Fig 11.4
Farm staff composition

Harare City Council Farms 1992

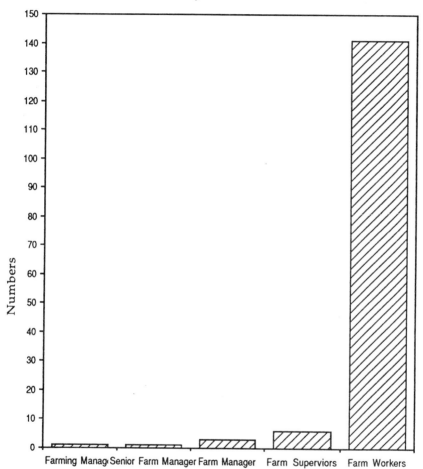

Type of Staff

to be disposed of on the farms. Most importantly, the Harare experience shows that conventional sewage treatment systems can be modified to support peri-urban farming. But community access to use of sewage effluent is an issue remote in the minds of urban managers at this stage. The first questions to be answered are whether that is a desirable direction to take and how to minimise health risks associated with use of sewage effluent.

Notes

1. The tend has now reversed with high pollution levels reported on the dams. Most of this pollution is attributed to industrial waste from Harare and untreated sewage from Chitungwiza which is discharged direct into the river system. The post January 1995 situation is therefore not as bright as that reported above.

12 The Cattle of Chitungwiza — Farming at Close Quarters or Friction and Conflicts on the Rural-Urban Fringe

Introduction

This chapter presents results of a preliminary study on the cattle of Chitungwiza — focusing on livestock grazing patterns, conflicts arising from cattle presence in the town and views of urban residents on the issue. Environmental health and town management issues are also raised. The phenomenon of cattle in Chitungwiza is a reflection of more widespread urban development processes which take up rural land without adequately providing alternative land for the displaced rural populations. Where the displaced populations are peasants without title to land, both colonial and current governments have not made serious efforts to find a more just development approach.

From the urban residents' point of view, it is not health risks which are the major concerns arising from presence of cattle in the town but rather the destruction of property and traffic accidents caused by this presence. Details of the review show that the cattle of Chitungwiza should be viewed not as a case of 'farming at close quarters' but as one of many conflicts on the rural-urban fringe. However, opportunities do seem to exist to convert these conflicts into benefits for both urban and rural residents especially if ways can be found to recycle waste water for use in irrigation of pastures. The chapter also gives pointers to areas for further detailed research which would incorporate views from the cattle owners. All questionnaires on this project were developed and analyzed using Epi Info computer package (a WHO package designed for Epidemiological Surveys)[1]. As usual, the author did the study on a 'part-time' basis given teaching responsibilities at the work place.

Introduction settings, problems, objective and methods

Chitungwiza, the dormitory town

The town of Chitungwiza with an estimated 1993 population of 5 00 000 (five hundred thousand) is located 30 km south east of Harare city centre. It is a product of apartheid policy during the period when Zimbabwe was colonial Rhodesia. Prevailing ideology at that time dictated for the physical, spatial, economic and cultural separation of black people from the urban areas: areas which were considered white people's areas. Thus to house the excess African labour population migrating to Harare, an African township was established within Seke through a government notice 795 of 1954 within the legal framework of the African Land Husbandry Act.

The Township was a dormitory i.e. a place where the black Africans would sleep overnight and travel to Harare to work everyday. Houses were basic elementary structures. There were no services or productive economic activities;- there was no desire on the part of the colonial government to provide any of these. With increasing population, the township was expanded through development of further residential areas notably St Mary's/Zengeza in 1976. The administration of the area continued to be controlled from the top central government. Even when Chitungwiza Town Council was established to manage the affairs of the townships (1978) and later at independence, the land remains state land and is allocated from the top. During the 1970s and into the post colonial era, efforts were made to create an industrial and commercial zone to act as employment magnets, thus convert the dormitory town to a proper town or growth point. In this regard, by 1990, there were 23 industrial firms operating in the town and the unique (Old Mutual) Chitungwiza town centre acting as the new heart[2]. However, the bulk of the population is still dependant on Harare for jobs, services and survival.

The status of urban animal husbandry in Zimbabwe

It is generally agreed and accepted that urban agriculture in Southern Africa, especially in Zimbabwe is mainly crop production with little or no livestock. In Zimbabwe the urban area as a livestock free area is a concept accepted by everyone including the person in the street. While the absence of livestock is a general fact for urban Zimbabwe, there is one town, Chitungwiza — where cattle are a dominant feature in the gardens, streets and open spaces of the city especially in winter and autumn.

It is alleged that a number of conflicts have been registered between the cattle owners on one hand and the city authorities and the public members at large on the other. Urban management in Chitungwiza for example argues that livestock in the city destroys property, is a traffic hazard, a public nuisance, and above all is a vector of livestock related disease. Consequently, with the assistance of Central Government's Department of the Attorney General, the Chitungwiza Town Council in August 1993 passed a set of Animal By-Laws to assist in managing the cattle phenomenon in the city. The by laws make provision for the impounding and destruction of livestock found roaming in the town and not claimed by the owner within a specified period.

The problem

Despite the presence of these laws, livestock continue to roam the town's open spaces and the by-laws have not been invoked even once. Therefore, management decisions and policies on cattle in Chitungwiza seem not to be working. This could be because they are based on assumptions and inaccurate information and are therefore misplaced. There is a need for policy revision to make it more appropriate and acceptable to communities involved. In designing such policies, new information and better knowledge of the phenomenon are needed. We have to assess the assumptions on which negative attitudes towards cattle in Chitungwiza are based. One of these is the view that cattle in the city are a health hazard. The basis of this study was to verify these alleged conflicts.

Why cattle in Chitungwiza?

The development of the town (outlined in an earlier section) has no relation to the cattle issue until it is translated into spatial terms, where Seke township and subsequent townships which today form Chitungwiza town were 'planted' in the middle of Seke Communal area. Communal people were either displaced or swamped by the rapid development of the town. Communal people are peasant farmers who raise cattle and grow crops during the summer months. The Chitungwiza phenomenon robbed them of their grazing and cultivation lands forcing them to be more and more crowded. No compensation or alternative resettlement areas were provided for these farmers. Therefore unlike the rest of other towns in Zimbabwe, Chitungwiza is surrounded by communal land and not by commercial (freehold) farms. In reviewing Chitungwiza cattle, this history has to be provided not only as an explanatory background but as a framework to seek solutions as well.

Research objectives

The objective of this research is to establish whether cattle in the city are an environmental health risk and to explore other dimensions of the phenomenon (cattle in Chitungwiza) which could yield accurate information needed in formulation of more appropriate management strategies. These broad objectives can be presented by way of a set of health and urban management questions that need to be asked on this issue.

On environmental matters, what are the health problems caused by the presence of cattle in the high density area of Chitungwiza? Is the incidence of 'livestock disease' in Chitungwiza different in any way from that of rural areas (Seke) or other urban areas (Harare)? What are the perceived problems and benefits of cattle presence in Chitungwiza? What are the residents's views on the cattle? Do they consider cattle a health hazard?

On non-environmental issues, why do we have cattle in Chitungwiza in the first place? Why are cattle by laws not used by the local authority? What are the ownership and grazing patterns of the cattle? What alternatives are there in dealing with the cattle issue and what is the significance of the phenomenon for urban development in Zimbabwe?

Methods and approaches

A number of steps were taken to collect both qualitative and quantitative information required for this study through literature reviews, discussions with council officials, the police and medical practitioners. Base maps were also collected for presenting pastures, grazing channels and areas that could be included for detailed work. Photographs were taken of some of these areas as well as the cattle herds while grazing.

A monitoring exercise to establish the grazing patterns was conducted over a ten day period using 4 (four) research assistants. This was to compliment initial field observations. A more detailed one day household questionnaire survey was conducted to establish views from the urban residents. Therefore results presented here represent observations made during a period of five months (May to September). In a case where resources are available, such a study could have been completed in a shorter period. Other aspects of methods used are included under each respective section where necessary.

Detailed results of general field surveys

Results of surveys: first phase

The purpose of the surveys (conducted in early May 1994) was to establish preliminary grazing patterns and channels used by cattle to access city pastures. This would assist in planning for the sample areas for the household surveys. The surveys also sought to make an inventory of health facilities available for input into the research plan of action particularly with respect to the health — oriented survey. Discussions were held with the city planning officer to solicit views on how execution of the survey could be enhanced.

Cattle were already grazing on city pastures and a number of herds were sited. The first herd of about 25 to 30 cattle was sited between Zengeza 4 and Seke Unit D about 1 km south west of Chitungwiza city centre. Off-plot maize crop had been harvested but sweet potatoes had largely not been harvested. The herdsman for this herd could not be located.

The second siting was in the north east between Unit H and Unit B where a herd was crossing Prince-Edward/Dema Road from the rural north into the town area. The herd boy was tendering this herd and directing it onto the town pastures namely a vlei area starting from this crossing point through Units A, D, C, J, K and down to Nyatsime River. (Map 12.1)

The herd boy was quite ready to discuss details of his herd and others he knew about. From this discussion, two other herds were identified with details given on names of cattle owners and location of their homes. These were from Rusere and Nyika villages. One urban based owner was identified. Located in Zengeza 3, this cattle owner has a modern 2 acre home. The owner was one of the indigenous settlers in the area before the growth of Chitungwiza. The herd boy had to follow the cattle to keep them from spoiling a well about 1 km away. This well is used by residents of Seke Unit B as a water source. Other herds were later sited in units P, M and O; all without herdsmen in sight.

From the above, it seems possible to establish the ownership and sizes of herds grazing in Chitungwiza. The task could be made easier if done early when headmen are still monitoring their herds. Herd boys/herdsmen are a good source of information and should be targeted with a separate questionnaire in future studies. One has however to proceed

191

Map 12.1
The cattle of Chitungwiza:
Urban pastures and grazing patterns, June 1994

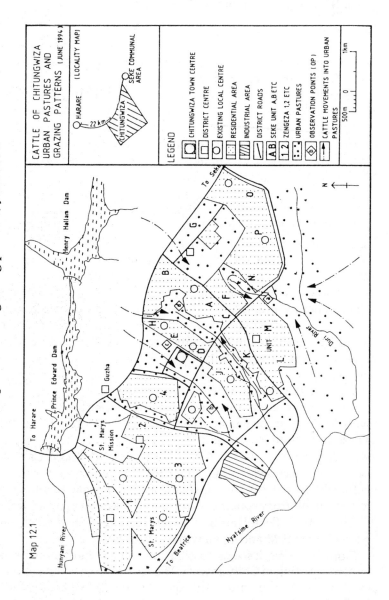

with caution until the confidence of the owners has been established. Herds are of large sizes as seen from above.

Questions for owners should include history of residence, tenure, and how their cattle survived during the 1992–93 drought. It is alleged that cattle owners blocked sewer mains passing through pastures so that the waste water flooding from the sewer mains was available for cattle to drink. Hence these cattle survived while others in rural areas perished. The city thus provided both pastures and drinking water during drought years.

From this case, if it can be confirmed, we get a dichotomous role of urban wastes. There could be a potential health hazard from the sewage water. But it is clear that there is a real benefit to the cattle owners. If possible such use of waste waters could be a starting point to initiate projects where the city and the people are partners.

An inventory of private medical health practitioners was also made during the early phase. Most surgeries and clinics operate during the day with nurses providing services while practitioners visit on specified times mostly during the evenings. A total of 25 (twenty five) private clinics were recorded: three in St. Mary's, 5 at Zengeza 4 shopping centre, eight at Chitungwiza City Centre and Unit D and twelve at Makoni Shopping centre.

The grazing patterns: second phase

The objective of this phase was to establish detailed grazing patterns of the cattle during this time of year, establish herd sizes and areas of potential contact with urban residents. These details were considered necessary to guide further work in the field. The study was conducted over ten days in June with assistance from 4 research students.

Strategic observation points on the pastures were identified (OP on Map 12.1) from where each research student would monitor and record herds on the pastures. Each student would make regular observations from the point: first between 6 am and 8 am, then second between 10 am and 12 noon, the third between 2 pm and 3 pm and the last for the day between 5 pm and 6 pm. On each visit to the (OP) the student would record presence or absence of herds on the pastures. If present, details on size of herd, direction of movement and presence/absence of herdsmen were recorded. All the research students were residents of Chitugwiza and each student was allocated an (OP) nearest to his place of residence. This way, the students could take part in the research exercise and still do some domestic chores at home.

From all observation points herds moved onto the pastures after 8 am, usually without herdsmen in sight. Occasionally a handful of cattle were found on the pastures at 6 am (early morning). The assistants agreed that these were likely to be stray animals missed by herdsmen during 'round ups' of the previous evening. On the majority of days, herdsmen would be seen driving the cattle towards home between 5 pm and 6 pm. With crops harvested on the urban vleis, the herdsmen had no serious need to be with the cattle all the time. However, in unit J and D research assistants observed urban residents chasing away cattle which had invaded backyard gardens.

A pattern therefore emerged where on a daily basis cattle would move into the pastures unattended and be collected for night keeping by herdsmen in the evenings. At the time of survey there was still water for cattle to drink in the streams cutting through the pastures.

The size of herds were quite varied. Generally from the north the herds were smaller (minimum eight and maximum fifty) while those from the south east were larger. Over the ten days, herds from the south-east[3] had sizes ranging from minimum 12 (twelve) to maximum of over 200 (two hundred). There were cattle on these pastures every day of the 10 day study period.

From the north, pastures between unit H, E, D and Seke unit B, A, C and K and between Zengeza 4 and Seke units H, E, D and J there were no cattle on the pastures on 3 days out of the ten day study period.

Therefore at the time of study more herds were coming from the rural south east than from the north and north east. It became clear from these observations that a survey of owners had to include rural homes in the south east and the north east. The residential areas of potential conflict were Seke units N, M, L, K, F, C, A, B, H, E, D, J and Zengeza 4. The social survey had to capture residents from a sample selected from these areas. The general directions of movement of the cattle also give us an idea of potential conflicts with road users (see cattle movement arrows and major roads in the area on the Map 12.1).

Plate 12.1
Open Spaces, Chitungwiza

Source: Author

Vast open spaces in Chitungwiza are used for cultivation in summer and as pastures by rural herdsmen

Plate 12.2
Herd Grazing in Chitungwiza

Source: Author

A herd grazing in the north east section of Chitungwiza, 1994

Plate 12.3

Cattle in Chitungwiza are a Traffic Hazard

Source: Author

A herd of cattle crossing a road near Chibuku Stadium. Cattle are a traffic hazard in the area. The herd boys can be seen closest to the camera.

The household survey

Three blocks, the first in unit J, the second in unit N and the third in unit B were selected randomly for household surveys. In each block, interview type questionnaires were delivered systematically with the assistance of fifteen students. Questions asked related to the tenure status of respondents, personal or household involvement in off-plot agriculture, contact with cattle, views on problems arising from cattle in town and what could be done about the problems experienced. Residents were also asked to indicate past action taken to deal with the cattle in the town. The questions were answered by the most senior member found at home at the time of survey.

Socio-economic profile of respondents

Of the total 112 respondents in the sample, 45 members were from Unit J, 45 members from Unit N and 22 members from Unit B. 63% of all respondents were female. This compares well with the sex split of 55% females and 45% males obtained for Warren Park 1 surveys[4], Harare. The age structure for respondents is as depicted on the Table 12.1 below.

About 32% of the respondents were lodgers or belonged to lodger families while 66% were owners or belonged to owner families. The remainder were other types of residents not fitting easily into these categories. This compares well with a respective 24% and 70% tenure status distribution obtained in the Warren Park 1 surveys.[5]

Table 12.1
Age — Sex structure of respondents

Age Group	Males	Females	Total	% Cummul[6]
10-15	3	5	8	7.2
16-20	6	12	18	23.4
21-25	7	10	17	38.7
26-30	10	15	25	61.3
31-35	3	10	13	73.0
36-40	5	5	10	82.0
41-45	6	4	10	91.0
46-50	0	5	5	95.5
51+	1	4	5	100

$$n = 112$$
$$spoilt = 1$$
$$mean = 29.59$$
$$standard\ deviation = 11.57$$

198

Residential space is generally used for food production: mainly vegetables during the time of survey. On 92% of the properties a vegetable crop of one sort or other was flourishing. This again compares well with the 80% observed in Warren Park low income residential area. Vegetables grown include covo, rape, onions, carrots, peas, spinach and tomatoes. Covo and rape are the most dominant. Vegetables are nutritious food used as relish by most households. By growing their own vegetables at home and not purchasing from the market some money is saved for other uses. A detailed quantification of benefits would need to consider input costs especially the water bill. An effort was made to identify home based livestock production. This was identified only on 13% of the properties i.e on 15 out of the 112 properties; a much lower proportion than that reported for Harare by the ENDA report[7]. Small livestock at home is mainly chickens (on 11 of the properties) and rabbits (on 4 of the properties). There is a combination of both on a few properties.[8] In terms of quantities the largest number of chickens recorded on a single property was 86 (eighty six) while a figure of 18 (eighteen) was recorded for rabbits. These figures show a low prevalence of small livestock in Chitungwiza, just as in Harare.

Off-plot-agriculture — Chitungwiza

Respondents were also asked to indicate whether they or members of their households had engaged in off-plot cultivation during the previous 1993/1994 growing season. A figure of 39.3% off-plot cultivators was obtained. This is quite close to the 42% off-plot cultivators for Warren Park in Harare. We also have to note the differences in sample sizes for the two studies (310 for Warren Park to 112 for Chitungwiza). However, these figures are much lower than the 89.7% purported in the ENDA report for Harare.

Cattle of Chitungwiza; grazing and ownership patterns

70% of the respondents had seen cattle grazing within their locality during the day of the survey and many respondents reported seeing the cattle everyday especially during the dry season. According to a majority (88%) of the respondents, the cattle graze urban pastures during the May to November period when urban off-plot crops have been harvested. Only 6 respondents were in a position to provide exact names of some of the cattle owners. In general (87%) respondents concur that the cattle are owned by rural people mainly from Seke and Mayambara.

Cattle grazing urban pastures have caused a number of problems with urban residents. The problems can be divided into two sets; those specific to individual properties and those in the public domain. On individual properties cattle eat vegetables, destroy property (including fencing) and leave a lot of litter. At night they disturb the peace of residents. In response, property owners have erected stronger fences or gone further (funds permitting) to erect concrete walls — durawalls — around their houses. This is the only surest way of keeping out the cattle. But residents noted that houses are an investment and a cattle environment lowers their property values significantly.

On the public front, cattle are a nuisance to motorists and accidents do occur. Residents allege that some of the cattle hit by cars are whisked away by butchery owners who sell the meat to the public. Cattle also destroy off-plot crops grown by urban residents. In recent years especially since the 1991/1992 drought years cattle owners or the herd boys block sewer mains resulting in the sewage effluent flooding the valleys. This keeps the grass green for the cattle to graze. During the survey on Saturday 03/09/1994 vast expanses of open spaces were flooded by this effluent. Cattle were seen drinking some of the water. Of course the smell was not pleasant.

Consequently residents fear for their health since the untreated water could be a source of diseases. The health status of the cattle drinking such water is also questionable. This is also a management problem burdening the town council.

However, treated sewage effluent (after complete oxidation) is safe for pasture irrigation as noted in the Harare case[9]. For Chitungwiza the issue could be one of designing a sewage system such that purified effluent is available to irrigate the valleys. That way the herdsmen would not have a reason to block sewer mains. This can only be feasible if the town council or the urban residents see a direct benefit from and are involved in cattle breeding in the city.

A general profile of problems cited by residents are depicted on Figure 12.1 where destruction of vegetables and gardens is top of the list. For those who recorded experiencing problems especially where properties are not fenced, the level of concern was rated as serious to very serious (86%).

What have residents done about it?

As noted above residents have erected fences and durawalls around their properties. Still a large number cannot afford this investment. They can only chase away the cattle each time they get into their gardens. Residents allege that submissions have been made to the city fathers but nothing has been done to get rid of the cattle. They can only speculate that some city fathers are stake holders on this issue. Some residents benefit from the cattle. Indeed the cattle are hired to plough urban plots, an operation witnessed during the survey on open spaces west and south of Unit B.

Cattle in Chitungwiza — should they be prohibited?

Only 19% of the residents feel that cattle should be allowed to graze on city pastures. The majority are opposed to the existing patterns and would want to see corrective measures put in place. These range from drastic exclusion measures, such as relocation of the rural peasants away from Chitungwiza to accommodative measures which should incorporate agreed modes of conduct between cattle owners and the city. Table 12.2 below summaries views of respondents by sex on this matter.

Table 12.2
Should we prohibit cattle on city's open spaces?

	Yes	No	Total
Males	32	7	39
Females	55	14	69
Total	87 (78%)	21 (18%)	108 (96%)
		n = 112	

Source: Survey 03/09/1994

A variety of other suggestions were preferred on how to deal with this perennial problem. These are depicted on Table 12.3 below.

201

**Figure 12.1
Conflicts profile**
Cattle of Chitungwiza

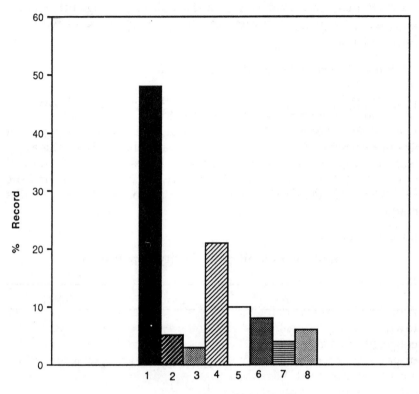

Destroy Gardens
Cause Noise
Destroy Fences
Cause Traffic Accidents
Cow Dung Pollution
Eat Laundry
Destroy Property
General Nuisance

Table 12.3
What can be done?

Options	Frequency
Encourage cattle owners to take care of their herds & monitor them	34
Impound cattle and release on payment of a fine or use other legal force	28
Fence round the city or other barrier e.g. electric fence	19
Relocate cattle owners away from city or provide them with alternative pastures	15
Provide paddocks	17
Provide urban fence to residents	2
Other	9
no suggestions	4

Responses from health professionals

A questionnaire was delivered at twenty of the private clinics in the town for completion by the chief medical practitioners and to be collected after a few days. The questions sought to establish major diseases recorded in the area and whether any of these were related to a cattle environment. Views were also sought on health aspects of the cattle grazing city pastures.

On visiting the clinics after a week, only three of the practitioners had bothered to complete the five point questionnaire. Appointments were then made leading to discussions with five more practitioners. This exercise required a lot of time and travelling resources and was rather expensive.

From these limited sources, none of the practitioners mentioned cattle presence in the town as a significant health risk. Instead, all emphasised that the cattle were a serious cause of accidents in the area. This point was equally emphasised by members of the Chitungwiza police whose records show a high level of accidents on the Prince Edward/Dema/ Seke highway. During the dry season these average an accident every two days.

Only one practitioner mentioned observing a cattle environment related disease brucellosis in his patients. It was not possible to quantify frequency of occurrence of this disease at this stage. Other diseases identified as normally associated with a cattle environment were tick bite fever, anthrax and mycobacterium tuberculosis (especially in HIV patients). The prevalent diseases are however not related to a cattle environment and these include dysentery, upper respiratory tract infections, tuberculosis and sexually transmitted diseases. Generally, one can conclude that the presence of cattle in the city has no apparent health consequence and that to pursue health issues from a medical point of view is rather expensive.

Concluding remarks

A visitor from Europe or North America, could take Chitungwiza cattle as an example of animal husbandry in an urban environment. This paper highlights that cattle grazing the town's open spaces are not a good example of 'farming at close quarters' because the cattle are not owned by urban residents. The cattle's presence is a reflection of development conflicts characterising the growth not only of Chitungwiza but that of many other towns and recently growth points in Zimbabwe (Nyika in Bikita and Nzimbo in Mazowe are good examples).

The paper has indicated that use of laws and forceful methods by urban authorities to manage this issue have failed. Residents on the other hand encourage use of regulations within a framework of dialogue between the cattle owners and the local authority. Of importance is that they encourage provision of alternative pastures for the rural owners to graze their livestock. All this assumes that cattle are not desirable in a city setting. Survey results also confirm the view that crop production in urban areas is widely accepted but not livestock production. Therefore laws that prohibit cattle in urban settlements are not as far removed from public opinion as others may want us to believe.

The presence of cattle in city environments can be made more desirable if the conflicts they cause are reduced. These conflicts relate to property destruction, traffic accidents and general nuisance. If mechanisms are found to deal with these issues as well as involving either the residents themselves or their local authority, we could possibly witness true urban cattle husbandry at close quarters.

It seems that the health conflicts are not very apparent from observations made and that detailed work on this matter is rather expensive. Use of the many private surgeries as a source of information, will require appointments with practitioners thus necessitating separate and multiple visits to the town. The chapter also highlighted use of home space for food production (mainly vegetables) and maize growing in the open spaces during the rainy season. These are activities where residents have direct benefit. There is a potential to exploit waste water for urban agriculture especially for pasture irrigation. This is a venture which would require full participation of the town council. The survey also confirmed general grazing and ownership patterns of the cattle. Further documentation is needed on profile of owners and their views on how conflicts created in the urban environment could be reduced.

Notes

1. WHO is the World Health Organisation
2. Opened in 1990
3. pastures between Seke Unit M, N, C and F.
4. page 9, Working Paper 6, May 1994, Urban Agriculture Research project, dept. of Rural and Urban Planning, University of Zimbabwe.
5. Working Paper Number 6, 1994, Urban Agriculture Research Project, Dept. of Rural and Urban Planning, University of Zimbabwe.
6. Cumulative percentage
7. ENDA Zimbabwe report 1994 (unpublished)
8 ENDA Zimbabwe report 1994 (unpublished).
9. Page 9, Proceedings of a One Day Seminar On Urban Agriculture in Zimbabwe, Department of Rural and Urban Planning, University of Zimbabwe, 24th July 1994

13 Urban Agriculture and Urban Development; The Futures

This concluding chapter cannot claim to be an exhaustive summary of the chapters in this book. Each chapter is rich in material of a different focus and can be a 'stand alone' piece. However an attempt will be made to go back on some recurrent themes indicating areas for further research where appropriate. There are issues to be resolved and pursued — issues of theoretical, practical and policy concerns.

Conditions for urban agriculture to thrive

A synthesis of both available literature in Southern and Eastern Africa and field work in Zimbabwe reveals that the nature, increase and prevalence of urban agriculture has been seen to depend on at least four conditions. These relate to national and urban economic collapse, land ownership and land availability in the cities in the form of 'public' open spaces or home space, urban management regimes, edaphic and climatic conditions and the food security situation. The decaying national and urban economies seem to be the umbrella factor while droughts and food availability or access to food seem to have acted as trigger factors in the rise of informal urban agriculture in Zimbabwe. The bulk of urban agriculture in Zimbabwe is rain fed. A good rainy season will witness more cultivation in urban areas especially if it is preceded by a drought year.

Broadly, the tough economic environment in Zimbabwe since the launching of ESAP has affected all families. Households have to establish extra means of survival and sources of income. Urban agriculture is one sure way of doing so. There is potential that everybody, the rich and the poor, can be an urban agriculturalist albeit for different economic motivations.

One of the conditions for urban agriculture to thrive is space availability. Conflicts arise between urban agriculturalists on the one hand and urban managers and other interest groups on the other. While town planners designate open spaces for aesthetic and future development use, the urban agriculturalists see this as an idle resource which could be put to immediate productive use. There is need to diversify our use of open spaces, create more space for urban agriculture both on-plot and off-plot. There is still a lot to be done in the policy arena to streamline strategies of managing urban agriculture.

Reconciliatory approaches needed

The city is not the same to all its inhabitants; it looks different and is used differently by those living in high density areas when compared to those in low density areas. The problem is that there is no consensus on urban open space use and value of urban agriculture as one use of that space. Sentimental, ecological, economic, cultural and recreational views have been attached to sections of open land in urban areas by the various groups. The groups are difficult to reconcile thus making urban management a complex affair for technocrats. There is need for consensus to be forged on how the city's local level problems can be resolved without disadvantaging some groups.

Institutional poverty to be targeted

Land management regimes have a role to play in the future of urban agriculture. So far urban agriculture has thrived where weak urban management regimes prevail and less so where development control is strong. But this opportunistic type of development is not sustainable since critical issues of the environment and urban economy do not get the deserved attention.

For significant changes to happen on this front, institutions at the urban local authority level need to be strengthened by way of resources and strategic decision making capacity in a way that accommodates urban agriculture. Of late, there has been a tendency by development agencies to by-pass this institution. Efforts should be made to enhance and not undermine the local authority.

The chapters also identified a need for change in policies on home space availability. Current policies are dominated by World Bank thinking on low income housing supply which view the home space as sleeping space and not as economic production space. Hence plots have been made smaller and smaller. This thinking is probably one major obstacle to increased urban agriculture on the home front. Coupled with this is the need for housing designs and technologies which conserve water and make waste water available for reuse at the local level. The issue of water is critical for urban agriculture in dry land cities and for the activities to continue throughout the year.

Environmental concerns need greater attention

Health and environmental quality of the city have been used as an excuse to maintain policies which prohibit urban agriculture. However such arguments are to a large extent based on conjecture rather than formal research insights. Aspects of land degradation, fertilizer hazards, diseases from livestock and possible consumption of polluted vegetables are aspects which need monitoring and research.

Surprisingly, enhancement of the environment through wastes recycling and greening of the city is gaining currency. Therefore, for both protagonists and sceptics of urban agriculture, there is scope to engage in joint research on urban environments. Consensus on the environmental issues is essential for policies which support the activity. As already indicated, such work should be extended to include research on sewage systems and water conservation in the home and the city.

At the same time, provision of expert veterinary and agricultural extension services should be extended to include urban areas. The destruction of crops by armyworms, newcastle poultry disease and the rodents menace in the early 1990s have shown the need to extend these services to urban areas.

On-going work in Zimbabwe has targeted the delicate vlei/dambo areas because of their agricultural productivity which makes them attractive to informal urban cultivators. Economic and sustainable use of such areas is our long-term objective. 'What is the ecological impact of cultivation in different urban environments is still a question to be answered in full'.

Targeting the poor is not enough

A dominant theme related to urban agriculture is urban poverty alleviation. Policies, strategies and aid resources follow this path and try to reverse urban poverty by identifying poor groups for assistance. Targeting the poor alone will not solve our development problem unless every section of the society is taken into consideration and is involved. What is targeted for the poor will be netted by the middle and upper income groups. Urban agriculture practices in Zimbabwe demonstrate how natural market forces have led to such a situation as upper income families who are pushed out of the formal employment sector seek survival in the informal sector. Policies for housing low income families have also met with the same fate. Houses meant for the low income groups are now occupied and owned by higher income groups through a process of downward infiltration due to policies which did not make houses available for the middle income groups.

The message for urban agriculture proponents is that urban poverty at the lowest level of society is not a viable entry point for the long term. Participation by all urban residents should be encouraged. The upper classes have savings which they could invest in the activity for the benefit of all while reducing the need for credits to the sector.

However, those components which target the poor should be thoroughly researched and be based on full understanding of the cultural, nutritional, economic and family conditions of the sector. For example if projects are initiated which promote cash crops or potatoes, then the poor in Zimbabwe would not be interested since for them, vegetables and the staple food maize are priority number one. Strategies have also to guard against increased labour burdens on the womenfolk who are currently overstretched. On the income side, the potential of urban agriculture should be compared against alternative money making ventures in the city.

Beyond descriptive studies

The literature and research on urban agriculture (some call it urban farming) is increasing rapidly. Most of it is however descriptive and does not give details on processes and linkages between this activity and other sectors. Detailed aspects of nutrition, rural-urban linkages, technologies and techniques, production networks and so on.

This book has made an effort to address some of the issues including the need for comparative and longitudinal studies which cut across city sizes, countries and professions. Specialists in health, technology, economics, engineering, politics, veterinary science, and urban management are now coming together to tackle the cattle of Chitungwiza issue. Frameworks such as RUPSEA Network (Association of Rural and Urban Planners in Southern and Eastern Africa) could be used as a platform to conduct region wide activities.

The opportunity costs of urban agriculture need detailed analysis since costs arising from urban agriculture are bound to be high in urban areas where all development is intensive and competitive. In looking at this aspect, community responsibility in managing urban affairs should be emphasised. Information should be available to communities with respect to implications of any choices they may have to make. Organisation of urban agriculturalists in Zimbabwe has followed the populist communal model. Such approaches should be made to exist and compete against individual or family ventures. In fact as shown in this book, while local governments promote the communal approach, in practice, operations of cultivators are dominated by individual and family approaches.

The 'story' as told in this book is far from complete, but it goes a long way in filling the gaps existing in the literature on Urban Agriculture in Africa. Harare in particular can now be compared to Dar es Salaam, Nairobi, Lilongwe and Lusaka to the north and Durban, Johannesburg, Maseru, Maputo and Gaborone to the south. Such comparative studies will however require that we agree on concepts, definitions and methods. The book has made suggestions on all three fronts in a bid to assist discussion on standardisation of tools of the trade.

Urban Governance - framework for the future?

As indicated in Chapter 2 and highlighted in other chapters (especially six, seven and nine) the institutional framework needs to be more accommodative of urban agriculture before we can reap benefits from improved technology, credit, comparative research and so on. The theme 'urban governance' is emerging as a rallying point for development dialogue in southern Africa in the mid 1990s. Among other things, the concept calls for greater participation of civil society in deliberations of government (including local government) on matters of development policy formulation, choice, implementation and use of resources. The private sector, communities and non-governmental organisations would have a greater role in determining use and management of urban resources such as land.

Giving communities a chance, 'listening to the people' may provide us with the solutions, more so if the people are given the chance to lead. As Iliffe (1987:1) advises;

" . . . the heroism of African history is to be found not in the deeds of kings, but in the struggles of ordinary people against the forces of nature and the cruelty of men . . ."

This may be a very extreme view which if recast in terms of urban poverty and management in Zimbabwe today would instruct us that solutions to these problems may not come from Borrowdale, Mukwati building, or desks of government officers but from the shackles of Mbare, Mucheke, Makokoba, Mufakose, Kuwadzana, Porta Squatter Camp, Warren Park and so on. Partly. The theme of urban governance offers us a chance to give serious attention to roles of urban agriculturalists in shaping the future of the industry at policy level.

211

Bibliography

Aart van de Laar. A Framework For the Analysis of Common Pool Natural Resources. Working Paper Series No. 77, April 1990. ISS The Hague.

Access To Justice for The Urban Poor In Southern and Eastern Africa (1994). UNDP/UNCHS Harare, Nairobi

Afshar H. (1991) Women, Development and Survival In the Third World. London, Longman

Artkinson P. (1992) Understanding Ethnographic Texts. Sage Publications Qualitative Research Methods Vol. 25

Bagachwa M. S. D. (1991) Choice of Technology in Industry: The Economics of Grain Milling in Tanzania. IDRC, Ottawa

Bennet H.S. (1956) Life On The English Manor; Study of Peasant Conditions 1150-1400. Cambridge University Press

Bentley A. (1987) Responsive Environments

Blowers A. et.al. (1982) Urban Change and Conflict: An Interdisciplinary Reader. Harper & Row Publishers, London

Bradford M.G. and Kent W.A. (1986) Human Geography; Theories and Their Applications. Science in Geography 5. Oxford University Press.

Brundtland Gro H. (1987) Our Common Future: The World Commission On Environment and Development (chap. 10; Managing The commons). Oxford University Press.

Cormack I. R. N. (1983) Towards Self-Reliance: Urban Social Development in Zimbabwe. Mambo Press,Gweru.

C.S.O. Zimbabwe: Women and Men; Facts and Figures, Harare, December 1991.

—— Combined Demographic Analysis Report, February 1992, Harare.

—— Zimbabwe: Combined Demographic Analysis Report. February 1992 (Draft Discussed at Workshop 2-3 March 1992) Meikles Hotel, Harare

—— Zimbabwe: Combined Demographic Analysis Volume I, November 1992 Zimbawbe 1992 Census Prelimary Report(s) December 1992, Harare, Harare

—— The Consumer Price Index: Release 12/12/1992, Harare.

Chambers R. (1984) Putting The Last First. Longman

Coleman B.I. (1973) The Idea of The City In the Nineteenth Century Britain. Routledge and Kegan Paul, London, Boston

Cox H.W. (1976) Cities: The Public Domain. Penguin Books

Cumming S.D. Post-colonial Urban Residential Change in Harare: A Case Study. in Zinyama L. et. al (eds) (1993)Harare: The Growth and problems of The City. University of Zimbabwe Publications.

Department of Housing and Community Services Memos: various as cited in text. Harare City Council.

Departmental Committee of Inquiry into Allotments-Report. Presented to Parliament By Minister of Housing and Local Government and Secretary of State for Wales by Command of Her Majesty, October 1969 (560 pages). London, Her Majesty's Stationery Office.

Diekes M, Weller H, Antal A.B. (1987) eds. Comparative Policy Research: Learning From Experience. WZB Publications, Gower (Chapter 1, 2, 3)

Drakakis Smith D. (1992) Strategies for Meeting Basic Food Needs in Harare, pages 258-283 in Baker J. and Pederson P.O. eds The Rural-Urban Interface in Africa; Expansion and Adaptation. Nordiska Afrikainstitutet, Copenhagen.

Elmastri R. & Nanathes B.(1989) Fundamentals of Data Base Systems. The Benjamin/Cumming Publishing Co. Inc.

Enerst R. A. (1992) Approaches to Planning; Introducing Current Planning Theories, Concepts and Issues (2nd edition). Gordon and Breach Science Publishers

Evans A. Chapter 2 in Lise Ostergaard eds. (1992) Gender and Development: A Practical Guide.

Fielding N.G. And Lee R.M. (1991) Using Computers in Qualitative Research. Sage Publishing, London, New Dehli

Finnegan R. (1989) Oral Traditions and The Verbal Arts; A Guide To Research Practices. Routledge, London and New York

Freeman D. B. (1991) A City of Farmers. Informal Urban Agriculture in the open spaces of Nairobi, Kenya. McGill-Queen's University Press, London.

Glass D. V. (1935) The Town and Changing Civilisation. John Lane, The Bodley Head, London.

Gilbert O.L. (1989) The Ecology of Urban Habitats, (Chapter 12). Chapman Hall, London.

Governance and Development (1992). The World Bank Publications, Washington

Hall P. (1966) von Thunen's Isolated State: An English Edition of der Isolierte Staat by Johann Heinrich von Thunen. Pergamon Press.

Harvey D. (1989) The Urban Experience. Blackwell

Hardy D. and Ward C. (1984) Arcadia for All: The Legacy of A Makeshift Landscape. Mansell Publishing Limited, Oxford.

Hindess B. (1973) The Use of Official Statistics In Sociology: A Critique of Positivism and Ethnomethodology. The MacMillan Press Limited.

Hirdman Y. The Gender System; pp. 186-207 in Tayo A. et.al eds (1991) Moving On: New Perspectives On The Women's Movement. Acta Jutlandia LXVII:I Humanities Series 66 AARHUS University Press.

Hough W.Z. (1963) Urban Life & Form. Holt, Reinhart & Winston,Inc. London, New York, Chicago, Toronto

Hyden G. and Bratton M. (1992) Governance and Politics in Africa. Lynne Rienner Publishers-Boulder and London.

Ilife J. (1987) The African Poor; A History. African Studies Series, 58. Cambridge University Press.

Information Sheets, Allotments Office, Recreation and Leisure Department, Meersbrook Park. Sheffield City Council

Inter-ministerial Committee for SDA Monitoring, 1993. Findings from The Second Round of Sentinel Surveillance for Social Dimensions of Adjustment Monitoring, Ministry of Public Service, Labour and Social Welfare, Harare.

Inter-ministerial Committee for SDA Monitoring, 1993. Results from The Fourth Round of Sentinel Surveillance for Social Dimensions of Adjustment Monitoring, Ministry of Public Service, Labour and Social Welfare, Harare.

Johnson J.B. and Joslyn R.A. (1986), Political Science Research Methods. Congressional Quarterly Press, Washington DC.

Kadenge P.G. et.al (1992) Zimbabwe's Structural Adjustment Programme: The First Year Experience. Monograph Series No. 2. Sapes Books, Harare

Kaseke E. (1993) A Situation Analysis of the Social Development Fund, Ministry of The Public Service, Labour and Social Welfare and Unicef, Harare and ILO (1993) Structural Adjustment in Zimbabwe. Occasional Paper No. 16, Geneva.

Kumar S. (1992) Subsistence Landlords and Petty Capitalists: A Theoretical Framework For The Analysis of The Production and Exchange Of Low Income Housing In Third World Cities. Working Paper Number 58, Development Planning Unit, University College London, The Bartlett.

Lambert J. and Rees G. (1985) Cities in Crisis: The Political Economy of Urban Development In Post War Britain. Edward Arnold

Lawson B. (1980) How Designers Think.

Larson A. (1992) Gender Research: Theoretical and Methodological Considerations. Paper Presented at The Workshop On Gender Research, Urbanisation, Planning, Housing and Everyday Life (GRUPHEL) 30th March -2nd April 1992. ZESA Training Centre, Harare.

Lee-Smith D. 'Experience in Research and Networking on urban issues" paper presented at the RUPSEA Conference on Urban Management in Southern and Eastern Africa. Lilongwe, 7-10 October 1991.

Linden J. van der (1986) The Sites and Services Approach Renewed. Gower.

Lynch K. (1960) The Image of The City. Cambridge, Mass, M.I.T. Press.

Lynch K. (1972) What Time is This Place ? Cambridge, Mass, M.I.T. Press.

Mabelreign Green-Ways and Drive In Cinema, Local Development Plan No. 20, City of Harare, Department of Works, Planning Division, May 1993. Harare City Council.

Mabogunje A. L. (1992) Sustainable Provision of Infrastructure: Issues of Governance , Empowerment, Participation and Non-Governmental Organisations. MDP Publications Series, Africa Region, The World Bank, Washington.

MacCormack C. P. and Strathern M. (eds) (1986) Nature, Culture and Gender. Cambridge University Press

Makuwaza H. How Recreational Planning Should Be Practised At A Urban-Local Level In Zimbabwe: With Special Reference To Harare, Bulawayo, Mutare and Gweru. MSc (RUP) Dissertation DRUP University of Zimbabwe.

Mangin W. eds. (1970) Peasants In Cities: Readings In The Anthropology of Urbanisation. Houghton Mifflin Company. Boston

Maseru Development Plan, Working Paper No. 9. Agricultural Land Use (1987) Physical Planning Division & Institute of Land Use Planning. Maseru - Lesotho.

Mate E. (1994) An Investigation into Land Tenure of Urban Common Land, with particular reference to Harare. Bsc (Hons) Dissertation, Dept.of Surveying, University of Zimbabwe (unpublished)

Maxwell D. and Zziwa S (1992) Urban Farming in Africa; The Case of Kampala, Uganda. ACTSPress, Nairobi

Mazambani D. (1982) "Peri-Urban cultivation within Greater Harare" The Zimbabwe Science News.

Mazambani D. (1982) Aspects of Peri-Urban Cultivation and Deforestation Around Salisbury (Harare) 1955 - 1980. MPhil Thesis, Dept. of Geography University of Zimbabwe.

Mbeki M. (1994) Africa and South Africa: An Interview with Michael Holman in Development and Democracy, Africa and Asia: Issues for South Africa, Volume 9, December 1994, page 3.

Mbiba B. Infrastructure and Sustainable Local Level Initiatives in Zimbabwe. Journal of Rural Development Volume 10 Number 4, pp. 361-375 Hyderabad.

—— Urban Agriculture In Zimbabwe: Implications for Urban Management, Urban Economy, Urban Poverty, The Environment and Gender. Seminar Proceedings Report, 24 th July 1993, University of Zimbabwe.

—— Urban Agriculture Management and the Urban Poor; Issues and Dimensions for Research, Harare Metropolitan. Paper presented at the Workshop On, Gender Research on Urbanisation, Planning Housing and Everyday life (GRUPHEL), 30th-2nd April 1992, Zesa Training Centre, Harare, Zimbabwe.

—— Urban Agriculture in Zimbabwe: Testimonies of Women From Warren Park - Harare. Workshop Paper; Gender Research on Urbanisation & Everyday Life (GRUPHEL), Zimbabwe Women's Resource Centre & Network, Harare, 2nd - 3rd March 1993 Harare.

—— Socio-economic and Gender Aspects of Urban Agriculture in Harare, Zimbabwe. RDP Seminar Paper, Institute of Social Studies (ISS), The Hague, The Netherlands, 1 st October 1993.

—— Institutional Responses To Uncontrolled Urban Cultivation in Harare, Zimbabwe: Prohibitive or Accommodative ? Environment and Urbanisation Journal, Volume 6, Number 1 April 1994.

—— Working Paper 6, May 1994, Urban Agriculture Research project, Dept. of Rural and Urban Planning, University of Zimbabwe.

Mies M. (1982) Fighting On Two Fronts: Women's struggles and Research ISS, The Hague.

Miranda P. eds (1972) Mythology; Selected Readings. Penguin Books

MLAWD/USAID, 1993. Consumer Maize Meal Preference in Zimbabwe: Survey Results and Policy Implications, Ministry of Lands, Agriculture and Water Development and USAID, Harare.

Mlozi M.R.S, Lupanga I.J. and Mvena Z.K.S. Urban Agriculture as a Survival Strategy in Tanzania, pages 284-294 in Baker J.and Pederson P.O. eds The Rural -Urban Interface in Africa; Expansion and Adaptation. Nordiska Afrikainstitutet, Copenhagen.

Mosha C. Urban Farming Practises in Tanzania. Review of Rural & Urban Planning In S & E Africa (1/1991; 83 - 92) Dept. of Rural & Urban Planning University of Zimbabwe.

Mudimu G. D. and Chigume S. (1993) Paper 4, Urban Agriculture in Zimbabwe, One Day Seminar, Dept. of Rural and Urban Planning University of Zimbabwe.

Mumford L. (1938) The Culture of Cities. London, Secker and Warbury

Mutizwa-Mangiza N. D. and Rakodi C. (1989) Housing Policy, Production and Consumption, A Case Study of Harare. RUP

Teaching Paper No.3, Dept. of Rural & Urban Planning, University of Zimbabwe.

Perraton J. and Baxter R. (1974) eds Models, Evaluations and Information Systems For Planners. LUBFS Conference Proceedings Number 1 MTP Construction.

Plummer K. (1983) Documents of Life; An Introduction To the Problems and Literature of A Humanistic Method. Contemporary Social Research; 7, George Allen & Unwin, London, Boston, Sydney

Portudal S. (1991) Seminar on Governance and Economic Development. External Affairs Unit: Africa Region, The World Bank, Washington

Poverty Alleviation Action Plan: The Implementation Strategies (1994). Government of Zimbabwe.

Rakodi C.R. Self Reliance or Survival ? Food Production in African Cities With Particular Reference to Zambia. African Studies, 21 (Spring 1985) pages 53–63.

—— (1987) Urban Agriculture: Research Questions and Zambian Evidence. Papers in Planning Research No. 109, Dept. of Town Planning, University of Wales Institute of Science and Technology.

Reade Eric (1987) British Town and Country Planning. Open University Press; Milton Keynes Philadelphia.

Report of First International Workshop On Gender Statistics (East, Central and Southern Africa), September 1991, Bureau of Statistics, Dar es Salaam, Tanzania.

Roberts B. (1978) Cities of Peasants: The Political Economy of Urbanisation in The Third World. Edward Arnold

Rogerson C. M. Urban Agriculture in Southern Africa: Policy Issues from the International experience. Development Southern Africa, Volume 10 No. 1 February 1993.

—— Urban Agriculture in South Africa, Scope, Issues and Potential GeoJournal 30/1/1993

Rubey L. and Jayne T. S. Maize milling, Market Reform and Urban Food Security; The Case of Zimbabwe. Working Paper AEE 4/92, Department of Agricultural Economics. University of Zimbabwe, Harare.

Rummel R.J. (1970) Applied Factor Analysis. Evaston Western University Press.

Ruthven K.K. Review Article 'Engendering Men' Journal of Gender Studies, Vol. 1, November 1991, number 2, pp. 185-189

SADCC Food Security Bulletin No. 6.92, SADCC Regional Early Warning Unit, Harare.

Salisbury (Protection of Lands) By Laws, 1973, Rhodesia Gvt. Notice No. 104 of 1973.

———— (Protection of Lands) By Laws, 1975, Rhodesia Gvt. Notice No. 840 of 1975 (No. 1)

———— (Protection of Lands) By Laws, 1975, Statutory Instrument 545 of 1979

Sanyal B. Urban Cultivation Amidst Modernisation; How should we Interpret It ? Journal of Planning Education & Research Vol. 6 N0. 3 Spring 1987 pp. 187 - 207.

Schlyter A. (1989) Women Householders and Housing Strategies; The Case of Harare, Zimbabwe. The National Swedish Institute of Building Research

Scott John (1990) A Matter of Record. Polity Press

Second Five Year National Development Plan (1991-1995) Government of Zimbabwe, Harare.

Sen A. (1984) Poverty and Famines: An Essay on Entitlement and Deprivation. Clarendon Press, Oxford.

Sheaffer, Menden and Ott (1990) Elementary Survey Sampling. Thompson Information Publishing Group.

Silberschmidt M. Rethinking Men and Gender Relations; An Investigation of men, their changing roles within the household, and the implications for gender relations in Kisii District, Kenya. CDR Research Report No 16, Copenhagen, (1991).

Small Holdings and Allotments Act (1908); Land Settlement Act (1919); Allotments Acts (1922, 1925, 1950); Small Holdings and Allotments Act (1926), Defence of The Realm Act (1) Town and Country Planning Act (1947) Her Majesty's Stationary Office London.

Smith N.J. (1972) Poverty In England 1601 - 1936. Harper and Row Publishers Inc.

Special Program of Assistance: Launching The Third Phase (1993) The World Bank, Washington.

Specter D.K. (1974) Urban Spaces. New York Graphic Society Ltd.

Strauss A. and Corbin J. (1990) Basics of Quantitative Research - Grounded Theory, Procedures and Techniques. Sage Publishing, London, New Dehli

Tagwirei J. and Geiner T. (1994) Nutrition in Zimbabwe: An Update. The World Bank Publications, Washington

The City as An Economic System - Social Sciences: A Second Level Course Urban Development Units 10-14, The Open University Press.

The Herald and Sunday Mail: Items as cited in the text and notes, Harare.

The Sunday Mail: Various as cited in text and notes, Harare.

THE Sunday Mail, Harare:

    (a) 15 th September 1991, pp. 8 Maritu Waga - Improve the Status of Women Under New Order (As I See It)

    (b) 29 th December 1991 pp.1 Uproar Over Maize Slashing

    (c) 29 th December 1991 pp.5 Critical Year For Harare City Council.

The Sheffield Telegraph, Friday 13 th August 1993,page 17.

Thorpe H. (1975) The homely allotment, from rural dole to urban amenity, a neglected aspect of land use, Geography, Vol. 60: 169 - 183

Tudor A. (1982) Beyond Empiricism- - Philosophy of Science In Sociology. Routledge & Kegan Paul, London, Boston, Melbourne and Henley.

Urban Agriculture in Harare. IDRC-Supported Project, ENDA Zimbabwe report 1994 (unpublished) Harare.

URBAN Edge Vol. 1 No. 1 Jan. Feb. 1988 p. 1-9

Watts T. and Brandsby-Williams W.R. (1978) "Do Mosquitoes Breed in Maize Plant Axils ?" Medical Journal of Zambia 12: 101-2.

Wekwete K. H. and Rambanapasi C.O. (1994) Planning Urban Economies in Southern and Eastern Africa. Avebury.

West C. et.al (1987) Food Composition Table. Mimeo, Wageningen Agricultural University, The Netherlands.

Wegner J. eds (1979) Images of Information - Still Photography in The Social Sciences. Sage Publications, London, Beverly Hills

Yates F. (1953) Sampling Methods For Censuses and Surveys (2nd Edition) Charles Griffin and Company Limited, London.

Zinyama L. M e.t. al (1993) Harare: The Growth and Problems of the City. University of Zimbabwe Publications, Harare.